Real LADY DETECTIVE AGENCY

REBECCA JANE

HARPER

We at the Lady Detective Agency take confidentiality very seriously. All names, locations and personal details in this book have been changed apart from those of the author, Ben and Paris. The cases described are based on real ones but any identifying features have been changed to protect our clients.

We do not recommend or encourage readers to partake in any of the investigative activities that are described in this book. To ensure that these tasks are carried out safely and legally, it is best to leave them to the professionals – you know where we are!

HARPER

An imprint of HarperCollins*Publishers*
77–85 Fulham Palace Road,
Hammersmith, London W6 8JB

www.harpercollins.co.uk

First published by HarperCollins*Publishers* 2013

1 3 5 7 9 10 8 6 4 2

© Rebecca Jane 2013

Rebecca Jane asserts the moral right to
be identified as the author of this work

A catalogue record of this book is
available from the British Library

ISBN: 978-0-00-748898-8

Printed and bound in Great Britain by
Clays Ltd, St Ives plc

MIX
Paper from
responsible sources
FSC **FSC˚ C007454**
www.fsc.org

FSC™ is a non-profit international organisation established to promote
the responsible management of the world's forests. Products carrying the
FSC label are independently certified to assure consumers that they come
from forests that are managed to meet the social, economic and
ecological needs of present and future generations,
and other controlled sources.

Find out more about HarperCollins and the environment at
www.harpercollins.co.uk/green

CONTENTS

Rebecca Jane started The Lady Detective Agency in 2009 at the age of twenty-four, after being cheated on by her husband. With her highly trained team of ladies, she now helps hundreds of people solve their problems. She was a finalist for Business Woman of the Year 2011 and was nominated for Inspirational Woman of the Year 2012. She also made the top 100 UK Mumpreneur list.

For Ben, Paris and Peaches

PRELUDE

'Is it eight yet?' Steph asks me.

'Not even close!' I tell her.

'I feel like I've been sitting here a lifetime; my bum is numb. I need a walk.'

All of a sudden I hear the jolly sound of a child-like jingle. It's an ice-cream van!

'Here you go, perfect opportunity for you,' I say to her, handing over some coins and sending her off in search of ice cream.

'Amazing! Surveillance is always made easier when an ice-cream man turns up …'

Steph isn't wrong. We've been sat outside the same house for eight hours straight, and we've another three to go. I'm pretty sure it could be classed as a torture technique.

My life is crazy. There's no two ways about it. Every day when the phone rings I never know what's coming next. I think I've heard it all, and then someone new enters my life. They have seriously bizarre tales and, more importantly, problems that need solving.

When I say problems, I don't mean things like: 'Who's going to make tea tonight?' or 'What shall I wear for my date on Saturday?' The sorts of problems I hear about, and end up deeply involved with, are: 'Is my husband having an affair?' (that's a very common one); 'Is the man I met online who tells me he's a multi-millionaire with boats and bodyguards real?' (not every day, but that one's blatantly another fraudster), or 'Is my girlfriend's house secretly being used as a brothel during the day?' (that may sound ludicrous, but you'd be surprised how often it occurs).

My personal life used to be filled with drama, but when the need for drama in me went away, it manifested itself in a different form – a detective agency!

A new client picks up the phone and tells me their tale of woe. I sit and listen. If they go down the emotionally distraught route, I put myself in their position. The same position I once found myself in – and I had nowhere to turn. Am I shocked or surprised? Not at all. These tales they tell sound crazy and dramatic, but they're all true. This is my life. My *real* life. Every day I find myself trying to complete the largest jigsaws known to man, putting together all the tiny pieces to help make some sense out of them on my client's behalf. We create a picture, and it forms the truth. The scariest part for me is that I think this is all perfectly normal.

Sometimes I wonder if morally I'm doing the right thing … You're either in Camp Yes or Camp No.

Camp Yes: They're the people I do this for. They believe in every aspect of our work. They appreciate the need for the truth and an agency like ours to turn to. They totally believe my life motto: 'If you've nothing to hide, you've nothing to be scared of.'

Camp No: They pretty much hate me (and our agency), and they make it known. They tell me that we entrap people, that we ruin relationships and look for things that aren't there. I think *they* have something to hide!

Don't get me wrong, I'm very firm in my beliefs: that we provide a good service to the general public and are helping anyone who asks for it. There are days, though, when Camp No get into my head. They make me question all my morals and beliefs. I'll have a little battle with myself about the rights and wrongs, but then I have to let it go. I don't believe I'm a bad person for doing what I do.

I created this dream and I'm standing by it. To help other people who are in need, to give them somewhere to turn when they have nowhere else, that's the reason why, right now, today, I find myself sat in a car with a fellow lady and friend who got roped into this crazy plan with me. She's one of many, and we sit with binoculars in hand ready to catch the cheaters – or the long-lost loves, transsexuals, missing relatives or, occasionally, a household pet or two. Every once in a while you can't help but ask yourself, how on earth did my life come to this?

THE MAKING OF ME

Back in 2009 I was faced with a choice that would change my life forever. I'd been unhappy for years, pretty much since I married my husband. Life had always been on the edge and drama found me no matter where I hid. I was twenty-four and the mother of a little angel, Paris, who was about to be three. Did I really want to become a divorce statistic at such a young age? Certainly not – it was my worst nightmare. I'd been fighting for three years to keep my marriage together, even though I knew the week before the wedding that I should have called it off.

Don't get me wrong; in the beginning James, my husband, was fantastic. But after we got engaged and I became pregnant, he changed. I'd met him in a nightclub and always knew that he liked to have a good time but I warned him that he needed to keep it under control if he was to hang onto me. So for a while he did. He stopped seeing his best friend Martin, who had the same party ethic, and didn't even take his calls for a while.

Life was great for about a year but after I got pregnant the best friend was back on the scene. When James decided I was being 'too boring', he'd simply pick up the phone and call

Martin. Then came the disappearing acts. He would go to work and not return home for three days. These weren't just any random trips; he would go to Italy, Spain and often Ireland. I'd come home from work and check if his passport was still there, just to get some indication whether he would be returning any time soon. He ignored my calls and texts while he was away, then on his return he acted as if nothing had happened. As if this crazy life we were living was normal. Eventually he mentally broke me, and I became convinced every man did the same thing and every woman put up with it. I thought it was just the way things were.

Next came other women. Rumours would circulate around my home town, the small Lancashire village of Barrowford. It's the type of place where everyone knows each other, and houses look like cottages from postcards. All the things I loved about it – the close-knit community and the pubs that were so gorgeous on a sunny summer afternoon – I began to hate. The pubs became places where everyone whispered behind your back, and the people I'd hung out with for years were feeding me information about my so-called 'wonderful' marriage. I'd hear that James had been seen with his arms around the local trollop, or texting random girls. It was horrible. The place I'd held so close to my heart was now filled with doom and gloom.

One day James announced he was moving out of our home. I was seven months pregnant with our daughter, and we'd been married for two months. It made no sense.

'Why are you doing this?' I asked.

'I don't like the house any more.' That was his sole explanation.

What did he expect me to do?

'You stay here, and I'll move back in with you when you find somewhere else to live. In the meantime, I'm moving in with Martin.'

So I found myself living alone in a three-bedroom detached farmhouse, totally isolated. I was miles from the village, and the nights were cold, dark and very lonely. It felt as if I had nothing but silence for company. I could have moved back home to my parents', but did I really want to do that? I was married, had a child on the way, I had bills and a house of my own. Why would I just up sticks and move back in with them?

The rumours around the village got worse. Now that my husband had moved out, I questioned everything. Was he really at his friend Martin's? Had he moved out because of me? Did he want someone else? No one moves out simply because they don't like their house; there must be another reason. My paranoia became so great I couldn't function. I went to sleep every night with questions swirling around my head, like a song on repeat.

James and I were still talking, and had no intention of splitting up, but I was hitting rock bottom without even realising it. I'd ring his phone on a Friday after work to see what we were doing that weekend, and it would be off. First time I'd let it slide; second, I'd start to worry; and after an hour I knew what the score was. He'd done it again – vanished. Where he had gone was anyone's guess. I'd crash to the floor, sobbing my heart out.

I was seven months pregnant. I couldn't cope any more. I needed to do something about my paranoia and find out what he was up to. I dived into the *Yellow Pages*. Scared and nervous, I picked up the phone and rang some private investigators. I'd tell them the situation, explain why I had suspicions and say that I wanted my husband followed for a period of time.

I telephoned three altogether, and felt far worse than I had before I'd spoken to them. They were the classic investigators, cold and hard. They didn't care whether my suspicions were valid. They didn't care how traumatised I was, or give any thought to my feelings. They all had the same attitude: they wanted to sting me for a ridiculous fee and get me off the phone as soon as possible. Some would only work for me if I hired them for a minimum of a day, some the minimum of a week. Either way, when they were charging close to £100 per hour, it was looking like a costly exercise. There were no guarantees I would get any information. I might even decide to have him watched on one of the days he came straight home. I felt more paranoid than ever, but I wasn't stupid. I wasn't going to throw nearly £1,000 down the drain with no guarantee of a result.

In desperation I called one of my best friends, Jess. We'd known each other for six years at that time, and had been through a lot together. When we met, I was working in my first job out of college as a marketing coordinator for the local nightclub, and I saw Jess there almost every night because she loved to party. Then one Sunday when I walked in to work, Jess was sitting on a sofa. As always, I was happy to see her friendly face, but the light in her eyes had gone. I said hello in my best cheery voice and asked how she was, but Jess shook her head. I sat down next to her.

'My mum's dying,' she said.

I honestly thought it was a weird joke. 'Yeah, right!' I replied.

'No, seriously. She went in for a little operation two days ago, and there've been complications. Me and Adrian [her brother] have just been at the hospital. They've said we need to turn off her life support.'

Jess's mum was a wonderful woman. She made me laugh and her house was always open to any of Jess's friends. Her father wasn't around and the whole time I'd known her, it was just Jess and her mum. They were inseparable and best friends. She was only in her forties and Jess was only eighteen, so her sudden illness was very shocking.

The next day Jess and Adrian went to the hospital to say goodbye to their mother and turn off the machine. A week before she'd been fighting fit and well, zooming around the house with the vacuum. Now, she was gone.

Next came the funeral, and every part of the aftermath. There was no one left to take care of Jess. She was on her own except for her brother, who was married. One thing was certain: a bond formed between us during that period that won't ever be broken.

Anyway, back to my call to Jess.

'I need your help. Where are you?' I asked. She'd been roughly kept in the picture about my marriage for the past few months, but she didn't know the full extent of it.

'I'm at a football match. It's brilliant! We're winning 2–0!' She was clearly inebriated, but I couldn't have cared less.

'I'm coming to get you – now,' I said.

Jess was confused but after a short debate, she was told I wasn't taking no for an answer, and one way or the other she was leaving the match early.

Fifteen minutes later I was parked up outside the football ground in my black Range Rover, which was my pride and joy. In my wing mirror I could see her running as fast as she could down the pavement. She threw herself into the car, asked what was wrong, and the whole sorry tale came bursting out. What I wanted to do was go to the pub where I suspected James was, and find out what he was up to.

'Let's go catch the bastard then,' she agreed.

Jess was always there for me, and there would be plenty more times like this to come. In the following weeks we often sat outside pubs, peering through the windows to see if James was there. Our first attempts were totally unsuccessful, though. It was time to raise our game.

Jess wasn't the only person roped in to help with the DIY detection plan. Stephanie and long-time friend Helen were also thrown in at the deep end. Stephanie and I met when I was a student, aged seventeen. We both worked a part-time job together at a call centre. The girl's beauty makes me sick! I've seen her at her worst and still she looks perfect: a total natural beauty with long blonde hair and blue eyes. Very small, and slim too! Lots of girls know they're good-looking, and use it. Steph doesn't. There's no part of her appearance that's fake. She even refuses to wear fake tan on her face (which I simply don't understand!). Men swoon over her. There aren't many natural beauties around any more and they lap it up.

Helen is a couple of years younger than me. She's a cross between a sassy type of cool-looking girl and a traditional lass. When we met some seven years ago she was working in a call centre. If you had to sum up Helen in one word, it would be 'complex'. Although definitely young at heart, she loves to entertain and behind closed doors she morphs into something else. In a former life, she was Delia Smith – I kid you not! The woman is a total home-maker, which is not what you would expect from her appearance. Helen lives on her own and has done since she was eighteen. There's no real reason for it; she's just highly independent.

Over the next few weeks we girls got up to lots of things we shouldn't. Nights were spent outside pubs in Barrowford with the car's DVD replaying episodes of *Friends*, bags of Doritos on hand, and the obligatory pair of binoculars. Six times out of ten we found James. We would watch him snuggling up to girls at the bar, putting his arms around them, whispering in their ears – and when he kissed one in front of us I flipped.

'That's it, I'm going in,' I said pulling on my stilettos when I was already halfway out of the car. By this point I was eight months pregnant and, if I'm being honest, it probably wasn't a pretty sight. I didn't care. I'd just had enough. How much more proof did I need? I'd heard the rumours and now I'd seen it. What he was getting up to behind closed doors, I didn't need to guess.

I pushed through the doors of the pub with a very frantic and disturbed bunch of friends in tow. James greeted me like I was something stuck on his shoe. He always gave me a look in those days that I read as one of disgust. Was it just my paranoia? I'll never know now.

I asked him what he thought he was doing, and he simply told me he was having a drink with his friend. The girl next to him was shooting me daggers, as if I was the one in the wrong.

'Are you going to go now?' he asked coldly.

It was as if I was living in the twilight zone. Didn't he realise I'd seen him kissing her? Did he care if I had? I don't think he did.

'Are you coming with me?' I asked, still getting daggers from the girl. How could she do that when she could see my huge bump? So much for sisterhood …

'No, but *you're* going,' he told me, standing up and ushering me towards the door.

'He's not worth it,' Stephanie told me, taking a gentle hold of my arm.

I wasn't going to embarrass myself any further, so I turned around without a word and walked out, leaving my husband with the girl.

When I was on my own, I questioned everything. If he was so unhappy, why did he not just end it with me? Why keep pretending it wasn't happening? What was I doing that was so wrong? Should I leave, and admit failure? How could I bring up a child on my own? I wasn't prepared for it when I found out I was pregnant, and now I was a month away from having the baby I still didn't feel prepared.

★   ★   ★

James and I had decided to start trying for a family six months before our wedding. I'd been on the contraceptive pill for years and we both thought it would take a good while to conceive. We were wrong. On holiday I started to feel sick very quickly, and I missed a period.

Coincidentally, the weekend before that had been James's first-ever vanishing act. He went on the Friday and returned on the Monday as if nothing had happened. It distressed me. He'd been at a concert and purposely ignored every call I made and text I sent. For all I knew he was dead under a bus somewhere. Was this a sign of things to come? I didn't know, but it caused a blazing row. I am normally a pretty calm and laid-back person but it scared me.

Now I was faced with the prospect of having a baby. Was it the right time, and was this still the right path for me? When I thought there was a chance it could be true, I wasn't excited or happy the way I should have been. I was scared. I went to Sainsbury's and bought a pregnancy test. I couldn't wait for the result so I went into the public toilets and took the test, then as I walked back to the car I nervously looked at the result. It was positive. What did I do? I rang Stephanie. Not my soon-to-be husband. I didn't do a little dance for joy in the car park. I rang my best friend. The whole process of this life-changing discovery was wrong.

Stephanie knew I wasn't very happy. If it hadn't been for the vanishing act the previous weekend, I'm sure it would have been a different story. Alarm bells were screaming in my head, but what do you do in that situation?

Steph said I didn't have to go through with it. I didn't have to tell him if I didn't want to, but if I did she was happy for me.

When I hung up the phone I sat for ten minutes in silence. But there was no question. I wanted this baby and I was having it.

I went to tell James, who was at work at the time. We both sat down, I showed him the test and … nothing.

'Great news,' he said after a while. He hugged me, and went back to work. Life-changing moment – over.

*   *   *

Looking back, nothing in our relationship had been right. So many little alarm bells rang. The DIY detective spell came to a very abrupt halt one late night in March. Our daughter was due in three weeks, and I was larger than a house. We were still living in separate houses, and life was getting no better.

Stephanie and I had been outside a pub watching James for a couple of hours. A taxi turned up at the door and he got in, with his best friend Martin. We set off in pursuit. After ten minutes we got the feeling something was wrong. The taxi had led us in a big circle through the village. It went down some back streets for no apparent reason. When it started to gain rapid speed, we knew we had been caught. Did I stop following, as I should have done? What was I going to achieve now? I didn't know, but equally I didn't stop. We were driving at 50mph down tiny streets with a 30mph speed limit, and it was crazy. Stephanie was scared. She was pleading with me to stop, but something had taken over me.

The taxi drove onto my parents' estate, where they were waiting outside their house in their dressing gowns. James must have phoned ahead to warn them what was happening. The taxi pulled up and I came to a halt behind it. I told Stephanie to get out and stay with my parents. A very heated argument then took place between my parents and James, while I refused to get out of the car. I knew he would leave again, and I was ready to follow.

James and friend got back in the taxi and sped off again. So did I. The pursuit continued, but not for long. The taxi lost control and slammed on the brakes so hard I couldn't avoid crashing into the back of it.

James sat in the taxi but the taxi driver got out and yelled, 'What have you done to my taxi?' Neither car would start up again.

James rang Mum and Dad and told them what had happened. They came straight away, still in their dressing gowns. As I stood by the roadside watching my car being towed away, I vowed that was the last time I would follow him. From then on, he could do whatever he wanted. This whole situation had gone way beyond my control and I'd had enough. I wondered if the constant need to know where he was had turned me psychotic. Did I need psychiatric help? Was his behaviour normal while mine was irrational? I didn't know, and I didn't want to know. My marriage was doomed. It should never have gone ahead.

James and Mum didn't talk to each other again until I was in the delivery room, having our daughter. Compared to pregnancy the labour was easy, and Paris was born in spring 2006. I'd found a new house by that time, and James moved back in.

For a couple of weeks, life was OK. Not brilliant, but OK. I didn't understand Paris. To me she was just a little ball of energy that had turned up in my life and I simply had to care for her. She didn't feel like she'd come from me, or even that she belonged to me. It all made no sense. Mentally I was struggling. Now I look back and think all the drama while I was pregnant contributed to my feelings. I'd been emotionally battered and instead of recovering, I was getting worse. I didn't even realise it.

When Paris was eight weeks old James vanished again, and this time it seemed to be for good. I didn't actually care. A handwritten note from him was posted through my parents' front door telling me that he loved me and Paris but couldn't live with us any more.

At first I was devastated, but that only lasted a day. Next I decided to apply for a divorce, but the solicitor told me you can only do that once you've been married for a year. I changed my phone number, and told my parents not to take any calls on my behalf.

Then James's mum began to pester me constantly, and after three weeks I caved in and met her. She told me James wanted to talk to me. It turned out he was in Spain. I decided to give him the benefit of the doubt – mainly to find out why he'd done this – and I rang him.

I remember that day so clearly. It was at my parents' house. Jess and Mum were in the lounge. I was in the hallway on the stairs. We talked and I interrogated James. His master plan was that Paris and I should go out to Spain and live with him. I won't disclose the expletives that followed. I've always been a big believer that swearing doesn't get your point across any better, but that day the words all flooded out. My short answer to his solution was 'no'.

The next I knew, Dad was upstairs in the office on the phone to easyJet and he'd booked me on the first flight leaving in the morning.

'You're going out there, and you're going to get him back home and sort this mess out. I've already paid for the flight, so you've got no choice.'

I tried in vain to put up a fight, but in the morning I was on my way. Paris stayed with Mum and Dad.

It took me three weeks to convince James to come back, and when he did he refused to live in our home town. He wanted a fresh start, and to be honest I thought it would be a good way to help us move forward with our marriage. We didn't know where we would live exactly, but we packed up the car and set off. First it was Scotland, next was the Lake District. I went into estate agents and told them we were in holiday accommodation, and wouldn't be leaving until we found somewhere permanent.

At the time I was well into a property development career, so moving wasn't too difficult for me. I found a barn in the middle of a field and began transforming it bit by bit into a dream house. On the surface, it looked as though I had it all: a reformed husband, an excellent career, the best cars money could buy, a beautiful daughter and everything in between.

But inside I was empty. The thought of death grew more appealing to me with each day that passed. When they visited my family saw straight through the façade and realised I had severe postnatal depression.

I couldn't cope any more. I knew I needed help, and fast. If I hadn't got it, it wouldn't have been long before I did something drastic. I wrote lots of letters to Paris telling her how sorry I was for being her mother. That I'd brought her into such a messed-up life was getting beyond any kind of joke.

I did two things to help myself. First I saw my doctor, who prescribed antidepressants. But when I told James, he threw them out of the window. He didn't want me taking them, because he believed they would make me worse than I already was. I spoke to the doctor again and told her what happened. She re-prescribed and I started taking the medication.

The second thing I did was a bit more twisted and irrational. Instead of ending my marriage, because I thought failure wasn't an option, I turned to a man whom I'd adored since I was seventeen. He was a married man called John. We'd had an affair previously but I'd finished it after I met James, and we'd not spoken since.

Eighteen months later, when Paris was still a tiny baby, I picked up my phone and texted him: 'Fancy meeting up?'

He was surprised to hear from me but said 'yes' straight away and the next day I went to meet him. He couldn't stop smiling, and he soon made me feel desirable again. I'd forgotten what that feeling was like. He wanted to know everything I'd been up to so I told him the basic outline of the story, but I left out my true emotions. I said that James had been cheating on me, and he was sympathetic and understanding. He listened and actually cared about what I was saying. It had been so long since I'd felt listened to by a man that I was instantly, once again, hooked on him.

Not surprisingly, we ended up back in a 'version' of a relationship that continued for the next few years. How clever was that? I had a husband who was unreliable and cheated on me, and what solution did I come up with? Yes, clever clogs started cheating on him. When it came to relationships, I still had a lot to learn.

FREEDOM

Fast-forward to 2009. My life was a mess. I was still married. I'd stopped looking for clues of James's infidelity, because sadly I no longer cared. I didn't want to know. Instead, when James hurt or upset me I turned to John. John listened, he understood, and together we led double lives. I had my life with James, and he had his life, then we had our time together.

For years I pretended that it was a carefree relationship, but the more my marriage deteriorated the more I realised how strong my feelings for John actually were. People may say they detach themselves from affairs, but I don't believe they do. I knew I had no right to feel like this, since he wasn't mine. Trying to swallow the hurt and pain of not being able to have him, while staying in a torturous marriage, hurt me even more.

Eventually it became clear that I'd fallen madly in love with John, and didn't love my husband at all any more. I needed John and couldn't imagine life without him at the end of the phone. He was the one person I thought I could always count on. Really, I was a mess.

My postnatal depression shifted and I began to love my daughter as I should have from the start, but I felt guilty for the lost time. I had a lot to make up to her.

Next, my career began to suffer with the economic down-turn. My speciality was renovating houses worth over £500,000. I was halfway through my latest development – a beautiful Georgian manor house in a village hamlet. The ceilings were high and vaulted and it had real character. I knew every single inch of the development. I spent the whole summer stripping back layers and layers of wallpaper, which is quite an achievement for a girl who wears heels 99 per cent of the time. I researched Georgian colour schemes, and what would have been traditional colours for the different rooms. Red for the lounge. Duck-egg blue for a bedroom. Gold for the dining room, and so on.

My mother was convinced it was haunted. One day she was lighting a candelabra in the dining room to take pictures and the candles kept blowing out. Later that day when she was relaying the story to Dad over dinner, candles blowing out miraculously turned into ... 'Candles blowing out ... and then a white lady brushed passed me ...' Bless the mother – so dramatic! (You just have to meet her for half an hour to understand why I turned out so crackers!)

The development house wasn't my home, but I stayed there when I could. I loved it, with its ghosts and history. When my finance company announced they were going bankrupt, they dealt me a blow I wasn't expecting. I had twelve weeks to finish the Georgian property, even though it still had no kitchen or bathrooms. Sorting out bedrooms and living rooms had been my priority. That was a big mistake. I had no option but to sell it or they would repossess not only that house, but my home too. James was with me when the news broke and we knew we had a serious task on our hands. His solution to the problem? He ran away and left me to it.

That was it. I was sick of the James saga. During this particular vanishing trip towards the end of 2008, he called with the
usual 'I'm sorry, I won't do it again' routine, but this time I'd
had enough. Through medication and my love of my daughter and John I'd grown strong. The kind of strong I should
have been before my wedding. I told James not to come
home. Our marriage was over. It really was that simple.

I filed for divorce and didn't look back. I wasn't even upset
about it by that stage. People kept expecting me to break
down, and I'd hear them whispering about me, worrying that
I was bottling it up, but all I felt was huge relief. I didn't have
to walk on eggshells any more. I could be myself and do what
I wanted, when I wanted. I looked at my friends who were in
relationships and was glad I wasn't them. I felt nothing but
carefree about the loss of my marriage.

★　　★　　★

However, my affair with John became a problem next. The
game was up when rumours began to surface around our
circle of friends. We'd been seen together a few too many
times, and people began to put two and two together. It was
only a matter of time before our secret was out. All my
conversations with John now consisted of 'Should we be
together, or should we not?' He'd say yes, he'd say no. I felt he
was basically leading me on.

I tried to draw a line. I told him it was time to leave me
alone. I'd got rid of my no-good husband, and now it was
time for him to go too. I just wanted a happy, normal life with
my daughter but John was having none of it. I kept warning
him that if he didn't leave me alone I would out our secret
myself, but he didn't believe me.

Then one night when Paris was three she shoved a necklace bead up her nose and it got stuck. I took her straight to hospital at 10pm and we stayed up all night while the hospital tried everything possible to remove the bead. I wasn't allowed to let her sleep in case it slipped down and blocked her airway so it was a traumatic night. Nothing worked, and she was booked to go for surgery. I was frantic to say the least.

Paris was released from hospital the following day, minus the bead! As I pulled up on my parents' driveway, after having no sleep for nearly thirty-five hours, my phone was ringing. It was John. We had a huge blazing row. If I hadn't been so sleep-deprived I don't think I would have done what I did next, but I wasn't in my right mind.

'I've told you we're over,' I said. 'Just leave me alone.'

It certainly didn't seem like he believed me, and I needed to do something drastic to make him listen. We'd gone round in a merry circle for what seemed like forever, going backwards and forwards. It would never end. We would have a break, and then everything would resume again. The writing was on the wall. I wanted to be strong and not go back to him. My stubborn side kicked in. I needed to make him hate me, to take the decision out of my hands.

'This is the last time I'm going to say this. If you don't leave me alone, I'll tell everyone about us.'

'Go ahead then – you do it,' was his reply.

With that, I hung up and logged onto Facebook. It possibly doesn't come any more immature, but how else can you tell an almighty secret to a vast number of people in the space of a few minutes?

All the time John and I had been having an affair, I'd protected our secret and gone to serious lengths not to have it exposed. Now I was doing the one thing I knew would make him hate me forever.

I turned off the computer, left my phone by the side of it and went out. I didn't want the temptation to delete my comments to overcome me. Knowing I had hurt the one man I truly loved in the worst way possible tortured me, but I honestly didn't see any other way out. It was the only thing left to do. Otherwise, we might have continued for the next seven years. It would never have ended.

I returned home and my phone was full of messages from various people and from John. I was too terrified to look at it. I instantly wished I could take back what I'd done, but the secret was out, and this was the beginning of the end.

He was devastated and utterly furious with me. I was devastated, but it was over. I deleted my comments because the damage had been done. I didn't need to hurt him any more. The scariest thing was that in making the decision to make the past public knowledge, I knew I was taking a final step from which there would be no turning back. For a long time I'd felt like he'd always be there for me at the end of a phone or email and now that could never happen again. I felt like a small child who'd had her comfort blanket taken away.

Afterwards I began to feel bad about how lightly I had taken the sanctity of John's marriage. My own marriage was different. When I started the affair, I knew what I was doing and why I was doing it, but I simply didn't take his marriage into account. I knew I should have – and he should have too. I'll never have a chance to put that right.

All I could do was look back and reflect on all the hurt and upset, and use the experience to become a better person. I would analyse the past seven years until the cows came home, then I'd mentally dig a massive hole and bury all the crap. That way I could learn from it. That way I could move forwards. All in all, I'd be making myself a better person for Mr Right when he did finally come along. And I truly hoped I'd be able to have a normal relationship one day without all the lies and paranoia James had led me to believe were part and parcel of a normal marriage. But in the meantime it was just me and my princess. And to be honest, that was all I needed.

★   ★   ★

I managed to finish the house I was developing by the skin of my teeth, thirteen weeks after I'd been given the ultimatum. I was a week over deadline, but somehow got away with it. I made no profit and my career in property development was officially over. I was down to my last house – the one I bought as a barn in the middle of a field in 2006 and turned into a home from nothing. It was secluded, isolated and still needed some work doing. I utterly loved it though. Paris and I moved into it, and lived between there and my parents' home. It was fantastic to have my parents' support at that time because, if I'm being honest, the barn was a lonely place where the two of us just had a few dozen sheep for company. I actually ended up spending most of my time at my parents' house, which meant they could help me out looking after Paris.

Next, I needed to find a new job and there was an idea that had been ticking over in the back of my mind for some time. I wanted to open a private investigation company. I had a strong feeling there was a market for it. Our company would be understanding and affordable. When people picked up the phone, just as I had, it meant they were going through one of the most traumatic periods of their lives. They needed someone who understood and could relate to them rather than someone who was trying to rip them off. People don't phone investigators for fun. When you reach that point, it's deadly serious.

As I'd found, it wasn't possible to hire a private investigator for an hour. Instead a big institution rips you off for at least a day's fee plus expenses at a time when you are at your most vulnerable. I wanted people to turn to us because we understood how they felt and would do what was needed at minimal cost. And there was no question that I understood what it felt like to be cheated on. I could have written a book on the subject!

The only problem was that after the property crash and my divorce taking every last penny I had, I was left with almost nothing. Even though I still had my barn home, an impending lawsuit with my soon-to-be ex-husband meant it could and most likely would be taken away from me at any second. I was prepared to fight to the bitter end to stay there and retain the beautiful house I'd made, but I knew it wasn't very likely. I may not have had the million-pound home or the fancy cars any more but I didn't care. I felt nothing but freedom and happiness. Mum pleaded and begged me to get a proper job, and I know I could have walked into most estate agencies and earned £30,000 a year as a sales agent – enough for Paris and me to live a reasonably comfortable life … But it wasn't my dream.

Dad understood. He said to Mum: 'Rebecca won't listen to anyone. When she decides she's doing it, she's doing it. Now hush up and support her.'

I had mountains of passion and determination. I just had to figure out a way to make my new venture work.

FINDING OUR FEET

'Hi, girls, how do you fancy starting our own detective agency?'

Steph, Helen and Jess look at me as though I'm bonkers but – to give them their due – they go along with it, even if at first I can tell they're just humouring me. We start throwing ideas back and forth, exploring the concept, and gradually they seem to start believing in it. There was never any question in my mind that they would be part of it.

I know that starting a brand new business venture with no capital isn't going to be fun. Let's face facts, though – when you hit rock bottom, there's nowhere else to go, right?

'Let me get this straight: we're literally going to watch people?' Jess asks me.

'Well, that's the idea!'

Back in primary school, I used to spend weeks writing scripts and putting on miniature pantomimes with my friends. We'd have 'big' ideas of putting them on the school stage and performing to fellow classmates, but they never actually took off. I know that the detective agency could be really good – no, *amazing* – work. Making it a reality was another thing. It could go the same way as *The Wizard of Oz* very quickly!

'Seems too good to be true, doesn't it?' I say to the ladies, tapping my pen on the table.

'It does a bit, yeah,' Steph agrees.

'But we have to give it our best shot. Something tells me it will work. People need the help, and we're the perfect people to give it. We know where they're coming from, and we've all been there.' I look at the ladies, and it's true. We've all been cheated on at some point. They're nodding!

'I totally agree. If it doesn't work, then at least we know we tried,' Jess says with conviction.

'That's more like it.'

'I just think it's really darn cool. Will people really pay us to watch their other halves? … I'm *so* excited!' Steph squeals.

It's hard work getting it off the ground. I spend several months producing a website and designing lots of marketing flyers. And I have to give Steph, Helen and Jess credit – they are genuinely amazing. They pound the pavements delivering flyers to anywhere and everywhere, identify key areas for us to market and help with the optimisation of the website. We all read anything and everything we can find about methods of detection: surveillance, background checking, DNA testing – you name it. We call experts and pick their brains. We spend hours on the Internet, getting excited about every new discovery. We live and breathe the subject and it's all we talk about between the four of us.

I have a gut instinct I am going to find this work fascinating. I never felt I entirely fitted in when I was doing property development or working for big companies, but a little business like this sounds like my dream job.

By rights this master plan of ours shouldn't work. For some strange reason, though, I feel it might just come off. We'll each work from home to start off with, and mine will be the main number to call, but I'll bring in the others as and when I need them. And we'll call it 'The Lady Detective Agency'. For years 'Lady' has been my nickname. Even my car registration plate says 'Lady' – something I'll have to change, actually, because it's a little too obvious for surveillance missions. The only flaw is that it sounds like we only help women, when really we want to help anyone. Men are just as insecure as women, and women are unfaithful just as much as men – I should know. But my gut instinct tells me the name is right for now anyway!

When we can't possibly do any more research, or read anything else about investigation, and our lives have become totally engrossed in the new business, we start doing some surveillance work for friends, without charging, and that helps us to hone our methods and work out where the pitfalls might lie. But still we haven't had a paying job.

I am almost losing the faith, when one day about four weeks after we first start planning the agency …

*   *   *

The phone has finally started to ring! I'm spinning round on my new revolving chair when the *Mission Impossible* soundtrack – my new ringtone – begins to emit from my mobile. I wonder if this whole 'private detective' thing is going to my head? I'm loving the training, and I'm loving everything surrounding it, but have to keep reminding myself that I'm supposed to be a serious businesswoman.

It's a lovely summer day in 2009, pleasantly warm but not too hot. I've spent the morning with Paris, who is now at playschool. One of the huge benefits of having free time is that I'm getting to spend proper mothering time with her.

Anyway, when I hear *Mission Impossible*, I dive off the chair, realise I'm feeling dizzy from all that spinning, and wobble my way, giggling slightly, to the phone. I don't know the number off by heart and answer with my usual bright and breezy 'Hello!'

'Hello, is this the detective lady?'

Suddenly I sober up out of my dizzy state and am on high alert.

'It is. How can I help?' I walk through to the office, taking my place at my desk and becoming a little more serious. Pen is ready in hand!

'I'm worried about my husband. I don't think he's being faithful.' It's said in a very matter-of-fact tone.

I take her name – Jane – then put on my best 'I care' voice and ask, 'OK, is there any reason you think that?'

'There are a few reasons, but mainly it's because I just have that gut instinct.'

That sounds scientific! Although I am a huge believer in gut instinct, I need something else to go on.

'He took fourteen minutes to get to work two days ago, and it should only have taken him eight!'

Oh dear! This doesn't sound like it's going to be good, I'm thinking to myself, while rolling my eyes. How can she be timing him so precisely? She must be calling him constantly to check where he is. I let it pass, though.

'And then, I checked out his car mat, and there was mud on the one behind the driver's seat.'

I wonder if this is the point when I need to tell her she's crackers? Everyone gets mud in their car, for all kinds of reasons. But this is our first client so I go along with it.

'Do you have any idea what you would like us to do or shall I talk you through our services?' I ask, trying to get a little more normality back into this conversation.

'I thought of surveillance, but I'm not too sure.'

'We can do surveillance. We charge £40 per hour, but if you're too far out of Manchester we would have to charge travel expenses.'

'I'm in Norwich,' she informs me.

'That's too far out of our remit to be included, but we could come to you for a charge of 60p per mile,' I say, making it up on the spot! 'It sounds as though surveillance would be a good idea if you're worried about where he is. Do you think he's going somewhere apart from work? Or do you think he could be straying at other times of day?'

'His work does worry me, and there's one girl in particular I have concerns about. Muriel. She works with him in the same office. There've been rumours before. His Christmas party last year was riddled with gossip that they'd been up to no good.'

'Who said that?' I ask, thinking to myself that she should have a conversation with the people spreading the rumours.

'Lots of people. One woman in particular I know well; she's a friend of mine. Although, that being said, she is also a friend of my husband's. She says they're flirty in the office. I know he is a very flirty person, and one of those touchy-feely types. Just not with me.'

'The thing to do is stay calm, and try not to let anything be blown out of proportion. People say lots of things, for lots of different and very strange reasons. Quite often they're not true. Until there's evidence one way or the other, you really need to stay level-headed for your own sake.' I try to instil a little bit of sense back into this situation.

Don't get me wrong – she could be totally right. With my experience of relationships, I've got every reason to feel cynical about men and their ability to be faithful. But her 'evidence' doesn't seem enough to get worked up about – yet.

'I know, I know. It's just he is *such* a horrible man. He actually hates me, I know he does. He would have some kind of affair just to get away from me.'

I begin to think we should talk to a charity or self-help association that will help us to compile a list of symptoms we can tick off to work out when a client is crazy and needs professional help, rather than a bunch of female detectives. Surely we need some kind of insanity clause?

'What is the most important thing for you to find out, if you can?' I ask her.

'If he is being faithful or not,' she replies, very certain.

'How sure of his whereabouts are you? Does he go to work at the same time every day? Come home at the same time? What are his weekend patterns like?'

'He goes to work and comes home at almost the same times every day. Like I said, though, the other day it took him fourteen minutes, when it should have taken eight. And he sets off thirty minutes before he needs to. He could be up to lots of things in that time.'

'Right, and what about weekends and evenings?'

'Most are spent with me or our son. Our son is very close to him, although he hates him too! He's eighteen, and he tries to get out of the house when my husband is home. They're more like friends than father and son.'

This sounds a bit contradictory but I leave it. 'Does he walk a dog? Or have a hobby?' I ask.

'No, neither.'

'Alright, so the main problem is work?' Firming up the situation.

'Yes. I think, because of the mud behind the driver's seat, that he picks up this Muriel he works with and drops her off. I've been to the garage to have his car cleaned, so the mud is gone, and if it turns up another day, I'll know!'

'That's not a bad idea,' I tell her, thinking it's a total waste of time and Googling 'relationship charity helplines' while we speak. I'm going to talk to a professional about this problem. I don't think she's sane, and I've had enough craziness to last a lifetime. 'Would you want surveillance on him going to work? What about at work? What does he do for a living?'

'He works for an Internet provider in their offices, but you need passes to get inside. I wouldn't be able to get one. He once took me there, and they wouldn't let me in.'

'Alright, so surveying him at work isn't possible. Jane, would you mind if I have a think about it and consider if there's any equipment we could get you?'

'No, that sounds like a very good idea.'

We finish the conversation and immediately I ring the charity I've just Googled. I explain to them that I'm an investigator with a new client, and I'm not entirely sure about her mental stability. Timing his journey to work by the minute, thinking he's been up to no good in the space of six minutes and obsessing over some mud in the back of the car … I may have been paranoid during my time with James, but I don't think I was ever quite that bad. The lady at the charity is very nice, with a lovely tone of voice, and she pretty much comes to the same conclusion as me. My very first client at my brand new detective agency is crazy. But what should I do?

In bed that night I feel rather uneasy. Do I bother to ring her back, or hope she just finds someone else to do her work?

Or do I get a grip, realise we're running a business and get on with it?

I can't tell her where to go! I'd once been that person. I'm sure when I rang the investigators about James that they thought I was barking mad too – but I wasn't. Is this lady the same? Or is it the case that she simply can't describe her problem to me convincingly? She is living with this man and only she knows what he is really like. Maybe there are other situations and problems that she isn't telling me and the story is all true. Or maybe she is obsessing over nothing.

★   ★   ★

Mission Impossible ringtone sounds. It's 11pm! Who the heck could it be? I reach over to the bedside table and look at the flashing bright blue screen. Jane's number is showing up! Oh dear …

'Hello?' I answer.

'Hi Rebecca, it's Jane.'

'Hi, Jane.' Trying not to sound too unimpressed that she is calling just as I am dropping off to sleep. We had advertised that we were open for business and accessible twenty-four hours a day, so this was going to be the downside. Maybe we'll have to revisit that idea in the business plan.

'I'm so sorry to call you this late, but I needed to tell you something,' she begins in a rushed manner.

'Of course, it's no problem,' I lie.

'You know Muriel, that girl I was telling you about? The one people are suspicious of? Well, she's just changed her profile picture.'

'What do you mean by "her profile picture"?'

'You know, on Facebook. Did I not tell you she was on Facebook?'

'Er, no. I don't think so.'

'Well, she is. I don't have her as a friend, but I can see lots of things she puts up. She's changed her profile picture, and I'm sure she's trying to tell me something.'

I want to *scream*! I really want to help Jane, but she's making it very difficult. Is she honestly trying to tell me that some girl she doesn't know, who works with her husband, about whom there have been a few rumours, has changed her profile picture to send her a sign? Really? How can I possibly work for this woman? I can't take money from the mentally insane! Sorry ... I'm no psychiatrist so I can't diagnose that officially, but from what I can tell, the woman is about ten sandwiches short of a picnic!

'I really don't think it's a sign. People change their profile pictures a lot. It's very common,' I tell her, trying my hardest not to be irritated or annoyed.

'But I've never changed mine in the whole time I've been on Facebook,' she says, sounding genuinely bemused by the situation.

'What I can do is add Muriel and your husband to one of our fake Facebook profiles. We use them to monitor people, for lots of reasons. I'll have a look around both of their pages and see what is on there. How's about that?' It seems the best solution to get her off the phone.

'Oooo, that sounds like a very good idea.' Yay! She's happy!

'Excellent, I'll sort it out in the morning. Don't worry – I won't charge you if I find anything. We'll just see what comes up.'

'Lovely. Oh, thank you so much. I'll speak to you tomorrow, yes?'

A momentary feeling of dread comes over me. Answering yes to this question guarantees we'll have further contact and I'll have to talk about this daft situation some more.

'Of course, speak then.' Damn it! I hang up the phone and write on the notepad next to the bedside table: Befriend Jane's husband on Facebook!

I roll over, turn out the light and I'm asleep in five minutes.

*   *   *

I'm in my own little dream world, walking along a white beach. Paris is dancing around in the shallow water at my side, giggling as she always does. Waves are lapping the pure white sand, and a fabulous cool breeze is blowing in our faces. The sun is beating down rays on to the shore, and I've never felt more relaxed …

'DUN … DUN … DER DE … DUN … DUN … DER DE … DE DER DERRR … DE DER DERRR … DE DER DERRR… DE DE …'

I sit bolt upright in bed! *Mission Impossible* is on again! I glance quickly at the alarm clock to see it's 9am. I can't have heard my wake-up call at 7.30am, and Mum and Dad have taken Paris to playschool today so the house is quiet. I'm scrabbling towards the phone, exactly the same as last night. Funnily enough it's Jane's number flashing up. Now I'm thinking it's either *déjà vu* and I dreamt our conversation last night, or it's happening again …

'Rebecca, good morning!' Jane says in a very upbeat tone.

'Morning, Jane!' I'm trying not to sound the most unprofessional sleepy woman that ever existed.

'Have they accepted your requests yet?' Jane asks, and then it dawns on me. No, it's not *déjà vu*, not a dream and yes, it is happening again.

'Sorry, Jane. I've not had a chance to check,' I tell her while slowly placing a foot on the cold wooden floor, praying the bed doesn't make creaking noises.

'Oh. Oh, dear. Sorry, have I disturbed you?' I wonder why she didn't ask herself this question earlier, before picking up the phone at silly o'clock?

'No, of course not. I'm just starting on some paperwork and you're next on my list.' Now I'm doing a cross between climbing out of bed and a limbo dance. My bed is far too creaky.

'Oh lovely, so I'll speak to you in an hour then?'

'Not too sure what my diary is like. Have you got email so I can keep you updated that way?' I'm praying she says yes and we can get over the silly 'phoning me every ten minutes' phase. That's an exaggeration, but it's how it feels.

'We can't do that. I'm not sure if my husband can check my emails or not.'

My heart sinks. 'No problem, I'll give you a call shortly. Someone's just turned up, must go.' Lying through my teeth. On the other hand if the kettle and toaster were real people needing my attention, it would be true. Either way, she's off the phone and my morning coffee and toast ritual has commenced.

I wipe the sleep from my eyes, take the steaming coffee cup and walk towards the computer. It takes me ten minutes of staring mindlessly out of the window in front of my desk to waken up. It may not be the world's greatest view I have before me – a generic suburban close on the outskirts of Manchester where my parents live that my brother calls 'God's

Waiting Room'. Basically, all the residents are over the age of seventy and live in large, exceptionally well-kept houses. They have money and refuse to go into old folks' homes. Their gardens are simply perfection and wouldn't look out of place on an American sitcom.

BING BONG! Snap back to reality. The emails have started … Best get on with work.

I have a browse through Facebook and choose three of our fake profiles. One is a very attractive brunette lady in her mid-twenties and the pictures lifted from Google images look rather provocative. That will appeal to men. Another one is a business – I always wonder if people are more accepting of businesses because they look 'proper'. The third is a man, again good-looking but not *too* good-looking. Women are scared of really good-looking men with perfect styling, so our guy looks down-to-earth. And then I wonder, since when did I become an expert in psychology?

Next I start adding people from Jane's husband Tom's friend list to my fake profiles, and lots more people as well to make it seem more authentic. I do the same with Muriel, the girl that Jane is suspicious of.

A couple of hours later, after catching up on the day's events via email, text and phone calls, I check again. Lots of Tom's friends have accepted our friend request, and so have Muriel's. What kind of name is Muriel? After some very basic snooping through their profiles, and a few Internet data checks, basically using Google and the electoral roll, I know a little more about Tom and Muriel.

I highly doubt Tom was ever good-looking. He is over-weight, by quite a bit, with a huge belly, a lot like Santa's. His face is grey and gloomy, he has greying black hair and his smile is missing a few teeth. His nose is certainly crooked, and his eyes are almost black. He's as far from good-looking as you can imagine. Beauty is in the eye of the beholder but surely no one ever accused him of it. Age: fifty-two.

Muriel. Well, she looks dirty! Not in an unclean way, but she looks as though she loves herself and will flaunt all she has got. Her profile picture, which Jane thought was 'a sign', shows her half-draped over a bed, sort of upside-down, with her fingers combing through her hair. Oh, and her ample chest accessories are on view, but not completely exposed. She's got sandy hair, dark brown eyes and a slight tan. Either way, sad to say, she is good-looking. Dirty, but good-looking! Age: twenty-four.

So we have a good-looking twenty-four-year-old and a dreadful fifty-two-year-old, combined with a seemingly lunatic wife. There's no way this can actually be happening, I sigh.

I click the exit button on the browser. It's time to speak to my equipment suppliers and see what we can do in terms of other options for Jane. I can't charge her a sheer fortune for surveillance when I'm 99 per cent sure this man isn't having an affair with the fabulously dirty Muriel! Surely a girl like her wouldn't take a second look at someone like him?

My equipment expert, Chai, is based in China. In the beginning I contacted lots of companies based in China, where all the best equipment comes from, but Chai seemed the best. He is truly an expert. He never gets tired of all my phone calls, asking about various bits of equipment and what would be most useful to us. He has great patience, which is what I need. I've always had a problem understanding accents, to my shame, so this stage of ordering products is always problematic for me. Chai understands me, but I still make the poor man repeat himself what seems like a million times. I already know the basic details of what I want for Jane's job but I run it past Chai anyway.

First we discuss hacking Tom's phone, which in reality is a lot less controversial than it sounds. 'Hacking' is basically a name for getting some software onto his phone, just like any other app you would use. We could send a link to our client, in this case Jane, who could then install it on his phone. After that we could get a copy of every text, phone call, photo, email, calendar entry and even his location from the phone. The problem with this plan is that by law the client must inform the person whose phone they're hacking before they install it and get permission. Or, if they own the phone, they must prove it to us by showing us the receipt. Jane couldn't convince me that she would be able to supply a receipt, or that she would tell him. So forget that option …

Computer hacking is exactly the same as phone hacking but for a computer. It carries the same problems with legality, so again not an option.

Chai and I have a chat about audio bugging. I honestly think this is the best option for Jane. She needs to know what's happening in his workplace but can't get in the building itself. If we somehow got an audio bug in there, we'd have no problems.

The other line starts to ring again, so I make my excuses to Chai and hang up.

'*There's a stain on his trousers!*'

'Hi, Jane.' No prizes for guessing this time.

'There's a stain on his trousers! *It's semen!*'

Her voice gets more and more high-pitched every time I talk to her.

'Do you know that for certain? Or is it a guess?' I'm trying to be a calming influence.

'Errrrr … well …'

Thought as much! 'We have testing kits, if you want to check if it is semen. Although it depends how much it bothers you.'

'Oh, it bothers me! I'm furious! This proves it!' Yep, still ranting.

'If the test is positive then you'll have some proof, but it may not be semen and even if it is, it could have got there a different way.' I really care about people, honestly I do, but this is a very big test of my patience. I want to shake her and tell her to get a grip. I thought I was psychotic when I was checking up on James but I certainly never went as far as to analyse odd stains on his clothing.

'I'll get the kit sent to you today, Jane. Try to stay calm until it gives you a result. It will tell you in the space of thirty minutes, so you don't have to wait for ages. Do you think you can do that?'

'I can. I'll keep calm and pretend nothing's wrong until then.' Then she launches into a whole barrage of stories about how much Tom hates her.

It turns out that they've had a very troubled marriage for a while – and when I say a while, I actually mean years. It appears the whole 'he hates me' business has some credibility. According to her, he tells her how much he 'hates her' every day, and has done for the last four years. He despises everything about her: the way she talks, the questions she asks, the clothes she wears and just about every other part of her personality. They've not slept in the same bed for the past seven years, and basically live separate lives.

Neither of them has any hobbies, and they spend all their free time trying to avoid each other in the house. Jane says she has tried to improve her appearance, and even bought some skinny jeans, but Tom told her she looked like 'mutton dressed as lamb'.

How can people live like this? Why do they do it? Tom has told her every day for years that he wishes he could divorce her, but he hasn't. I wonder why? Is she financially a lot better off than him, or is she hiding a secret of his? And why doesn't she walk out on him? Either way, it's very strange.

On the other hand, my own divorce is still an immense battleground. I've tried the polite and civil route for the sake of Paris. When I first decided to divorce James, I had visions of my future life. I would live on my own with Paris in a nice home, not extravagant like I've been used to – but normal, easy to manage and lovely. Think picturesque cottage with roses around the door! I'd work a normal job, he'd come and pick her up and spend time with her. All would be friendly and amicable. No hard feelings, just a marriage that didn't work and we could both move on like adults. Wrong!

He won't agree to the divorce, legally or financially, and we keep going round in circles with solicitors and courts. In my opinion he's certainly not kept up his duties to his daughter either.

So I know from my own experience that divorce is traumatic but I really think that, rather than hire a private investigator, Jane and Tom would be better off just spending the money on divorcing each other. For some reason, though, neither of them has taken any steps towards this, so here I am, involved in this messy situation. After over ninety minutes on the phone, Jane has utterly drained me.

After I hang up, I log back onto Facebook and see that Tom has accepted our friend request. I have a look through his profile, all the way back to when he joined. There's absolutely nothing of any interest. Not a single clue. There are only a few odd status updates: 'I love my wife so much, I am very lucky'; 'My family mean more to me than anything'; 'Jane has been the making of the man I am'.

Clearly Jane herself wrote these status updates! He's definitely not written them off his own back given what she's told us about their marriage. Why would she do something like that? If he is up to anything, and was using Facebook to conduct an extramarital affair, he certainly won't be using it now that he knows she has access to it! This is why clients' DIY detective stuff is simply a pain. It does nothing but raise suspicion and make our jobs harder. If she hadn't done that, he would be a lot less suspicious and we could perhaps have found out something interesting through his profile. I huff, puff and place the order for the body fluid detection kit – something else I had found by Googling. Then I slam the laptop lid down and retreat back to the kitchen, and particularly the kettle … I need a cup of tea!

*   *   *

A couple of days later, I'm sound asleep in my bed. This time in my dreams I'm up in the Scottish Highlands, staying in a beautiful castle hotel. The spa facilities are amazing, and I'm sat by the tranquil pool while Paris is splashing in the children's pool, giggling away to herself. I'm even smiling in my sleep, this little scene makes me so happy. I hear a buzzing, a bit like a fly but bigger than that. I can't put my finger on what it is, but it's getting louder. It's ruining my happy place.

I'm flapping my hands around my ears, trying to swat the fly. But it's not a fly. Now it's sounding almost like a song. A tune. I can't make it out … and then it clicks. I grab the pillow from the cold side of the bed and hold it tightly over my ears. If I ignore it, it will go away … But it's not going away. It stops and starts again. It's my stupid *Mission Impossible* ring tone. Boy, do I need to change it!

Huffing, I sit up in bed, a bit like a princess having a very pathetic princess-style strop. My arms are crossed, and I don't want to answer the phone … but I do anyway.

'Hello.' I'm sounding a little grumpy about answering, considering it's (have a look at the clock) 7.30am! *What on earth!*

'Rebecca? It's Jane. I have the kit. What do I do now?'

Oh my goodness. How do I tell her politely to go away?

'There are instructions in the box. What do they say?' Reading instructions would be far too easy for her. Instead she picks up the 'let's piss off Rebecca hotline'. I fall sideways onto the pillows and close my eyes. Jane may be on the other end of the phone, but if I block her out this could all be part of a bad dream. Squeeze my eyes shut …

'They say to run the stick over the item, followed by some liquid stuff that's got to go on it.'

My eyes are wide open and, nope, she's still there! She's on the end of a phone, but she may as well be sat at the bottom of my bed poking my feet for how annoying she is.

'OK, so do that then.'

'I've done that already. Now what?'

'How long does it say the test will take?' If I stay matter-of-fact, these conversations could possibly last less than an hour. I don't need a repeat of the ninety-minute marathon one.

'Thirty minutes.'

'How long has it been on?'

'Two minutes.'

'OK, so wait another twenty-eight minutes and see how it goes. Any problems, ring me back, OK?'

'Of course, thank you.' And she hangs up. I can breathe a sigh of relief.

My eyes close again and I'm being transported once more. I'm on an aeroplane, on my way to New York. A boy from school is sat next to me, and I wonder if that's a sign?

The phone … ringing … *Mission Impossible* … again … and it dawns on me. Mission impossible. I've jinxed myself. This is mission impossible.

'It's negative,' Jane tells me, and I'm not surprised.

'Ah,' I say. Very productive.

'I know. But how accurate are these things? I was so sure.'

Oh dear no, please no, don't let me have to go into an hour-long conversation about how accurate the tests are. There's no pleasing the woman; she won't believe me.

'Very accurate. I spoke with my equipment supplier yesterday,' I tell her, dodging the question neatly.

'Oh really, what did he suggest?'

'He said that the best thing would be an audio device, and I'm inclined to agree. You can't get into Tom's office, and neither can we, but if you place this item somewhere you'll be able to hear everything that goes on in the vicinity. Or else you can leave it entirely up to us and we'll monitor it for you and document the findings.'

'That sounds like a good idea.' After that she was on the phone for at least an hour wanting to know how the audio device works, how long it works for, how much it will cost.

Followed by what a miserable life she has because of him, and all the rest of the things we've gone through a thousand times since I took on her case. Suddenly it dawns on me why solicitors charge for phone calls.

The same constantly needy Jane calls me goodness knows how many times over the next three days, which is how long it takes for her audio equipment to get to me. Chai, thankfully, is amazing at shipping quickly. Goodness knows how I'd have coped with this woman if he wasn't.

At this stage I can honestly say I think she's crazy and that her husband isn't up to anything. The things she's worrying over are, for want of a better word, pathetic. Still, as our new motto goes, everyone needs help, regardless of finances or circumstances. If this is helping her, who am I to argue? Without any doubt, where I've gone very wrong is in letting her use me as a counsellor. That's something I'm not. She's been telling me so many horrible things, I honestly believe she is suffering some form of mental torture from her husband. I've told her speak to a professional and get help but she doesn't seem to take it in. Instead she rings me at the stupidest hours of the day and night and tells me everything. Very sad really. As much as she cheeses me off, I do have a soft spot for her.

We've had lots of conversations over the last couple of days. I made it very clear to her that if she was going to use the device she needed to tell him, otherwise, as I advised her, it would be illegal. Initially Jane was going to put the device in his car, but then she changed her mind. Then she decided on the garage, because he takes all his phone calls in there, but then she changed her mind. Next, she was going to put it in the lounge and go away for a few days, but then she changed her mind. Finally, we settled on a place. Jane was going to take the matchbox-size device and sew it into his laptop bag. That way it would be with him in the car, and in his workplace. No way would he be able to find it.

Two days later, at 8am in the morning, I start to listen in, typing up notes on what I hear.

8am – 'And you are gold – GOLD – Always believe in your soooooouuuullllll … You got the power to know!' Nope, singing. Not up to anything.

9am – all quiet. He was in a morning briefing.

10am – still in the briefing.

11am – tap tap tapping away. He's typing.

12pm – chatting to a co-worker (male) about what sandwich to have for lunch. Yawn.

1pm – chatting to another co-worker about a PowerPoint presentation for tomorrow morning.

2pm – tap tap tapping away again.

3pm – OH … MY … GOD! Er, what I'm listening to is very rude! Don't want to type it, so I switch to record. Dirty sex noises are all I can hear. Lots of 'oh my's, 'wow, do that some more' and the list goes on … and then I hear 'Come on, Muriel, now, now …' Well, that confirms who it is. I'm sat at my desk, quite close to throwing up. My hand is over my mouth, and my head is bowed. I'm literally stunned to silence. The one problem about these audio bugs is that I've got no visuals, so I have no idea where on earth they are! They could be in his office, in a hotel room or even in a broom cupboard. All I know is that his wife will not be happy!

I have to carry on listening though. I need to hear the whole thing, and hopefully get some confirmation this is still him. Then it happens …

'Please can we not leave it so long next time, Tom? I really miss you when I can't see you,' says the female voice.

'I know. It's just Jane's been really suspicious lately. I need her to chill out for a bit. She seems to be getting better just the last few days.'

Thank you, Tom. Everything is confirmed and I've got it recorded. They continue their conversation, but not for long. It ends with Muriel telling Tom he should leave his annoying, pathetic wife, to which he gives a non-committal grunt.

I try to detach myself from the situation and not think about what's happened. I pick up the phone and dial Jane's number. I feel horrible. He really is everything she's said. He is a dreadful man, who's mentally torturing her. He's having an affair with a girl young enough to be his daughter, and it seems he truly does hate his wife. Jane shouldn't have to live with this awful reality.

I break the news to her, and even though I feel sick to the stomach and deeply distressed about it, Jane takes it all very well. She's been totally crazy the whole time – but now she is calm? It's very bizarre, but she seems at peace by the time our conversation ends. You can literally hear the sound of relief in her tone as she says, 'It's not just me then?'

A little bit of my heart breaks, and I struggle to swallow the lump in my throat.

'No, Jane, it's not you. You were right.'

Jane thanks me, and as we end our conversation, I tell her I'll call her in a few days to see how she's doing.

*   *   *

I sit in the same place I did just a few days ago, looking out at God's Waiting Room, watching the world go by. I had been utterly convinced Jane was a total fruitcake. She'd driven me to the brink of distraction and I'm sure she was doing the same to her husband. I was 100 per cent, totally, massively convinced beyond any doubt that her suspicions were all in her head. What does that say? Does it mean that her husband is a typical nasty horrible man, a serial cheater and the type of person no one should have anything to do with? Or is the result, and my problem with this case, based on guilt?

I feel dreadful for not believing Jane. My gut instinct was wrong. This was the classic woman I'd set out to help, and every step of the way I'd doubted her. Had it ever shown in my voice? Did she know I believed she was crazy? I put my hand on my heart and hoped she hadn't.

It makes me even more determined to stay open-minded and non-judgemental when our next job comes along. And I'm hoping that will be soon. Because despite all the long hours on the phone and the many irritations, I feel I am cut out for this role. Just a bit more practice and I hope I'll even get good at it. After all, I have the credentials from my life experience. I know what it feels like – on both sides of the fence.

THE LADIES VERSUS THE CSA

I've got strong moral values – but there are times when they have to go out of the window. I've always been the type of person to hold a firm opinion – but on the other hand, I'll do what it takes to get a job done. If you ask me how ruthless I am, my automatic reply would be: 'I'm lethal. I will literally do anything to get to where I want to be.'

Being a Lady Detective, even for the short time I've been doing it, has taught me a lot about myself that I never suspected. One: I want everything my own way. Two: I'm a serious control freak, and the hardest thing for me is delegating my precious clients to other people. Three: my moral boundaries are still being developed. I thought I knew who I was and what I believed in, but almost every day I have to re-evaluate. Four: I am seriously fascinated by people; I have a burning need to understand the world and why people do what they do. Five: I never realised how judgemental I was! Six: I care too much (hmm, most of the time, anyway!). Seven: I'm really not very 'lethal' at all – in fact, it's highly possible I'm a total pussycat pushover … I'm still working this point out. Eight: I get infuriated with the Child Support Agency …

It's 11am and God's Waiting Room is as lively as ever. Mrs Jones is weeding her garden. Mr Thomson across the road is mowing his lawn, and Albert is talking to his cat. Quite a remarkable sight, three people outside all at once! I'm in a thoughtful mood. How can I expand the work we're doing? What other avenues can we pursue? So far we've only had business from women who want us to follow their menfolk and find proof of infidelities, and mostly we've succeeded. It seems women's instincts about this are often spot-on. Maybe they don't ring us until they are pretty certain, but all this sordid stuff could quite possibly mash my brain after a while. We need to use our services for good purposes, but I'm lost as to what exactly. The percolator has finished making my morning coffee, and tapping my pen on the notepad isn't getting me very far. I stand up in a huff, mainly with myself. Like a flashing beacon, the phone sounds. I've now moved on to the James Bond theme tune, mainly because I couldn't find *Cagney and Lacey*.

'Good morning, the Agency,' I say, in my business tone.

'Hello. I have a problem I need some help with.'

This is the point at which I'm listening hard. It could be a perfectly normal person with a very normal problem or we could be taking a step on the crazy train, and dealing with the utterly bizarre. We get both in equal measure, I've found. What is today bringing me?

'Of course, and we're the right place for that,' I tell the lady on the end of the phone. My non-judgemental (cough, cough) summing-up, based on her voice alone? I reckon she's in her mid-forties with blonde highlighted hair.

'Excellent. I need to hire a private investigator to catch out my ex-husband.'

'Really? OK, how's about you give me some background information and I'll tell you if I can help.'

'Of course. My name's Sarah. I left my husband three years ago and we're now divorced. We have a child – she's now six – and he's never paid child support. I don't want millions from him, I just want something. I don't understand why he thinks that my paying for everything is acceptable when we created her together. Not only that, I'm a single mother and I do actually need help. I don't have a money tree in the garden or anything.'

'I understand. It certainly doesn't seem very fair. Have you got the CSA involved?' I ask, wondering if she has a genuine case.

'Yes. I first asked them to look into it two years ago, and they put him through assessment. He never replied to any of their letters, so they based the amount of money I was owed on some chart or scheme or something.'

'I've heard about that. It's a survey they look at if they can't get information from the non-resident parent, or can't find a tax return. The survey tells them what the person is expected to earn, based on their job title. The judgment is based on this.'

'Exactly. It said I was owed £50 per week, which was fine by me. Only problem was that when they started to pester him for money, he suddenly replied. He said he wasn't working, and that he lives with his parents.'

'Is that true?'

'No. He lives with his new girlfriend, and I know he works. He has his own business.'

Over the years I've heard a lot about people struggling to get maintenance payments from non-resident parents. Maybe this is an interesting new avenue for The Lady Detective Agency. Just what I was looking for!

'Sounds familiar. What do you know about his work, and what evidence do you have?'

'I don't have any evidence. That's my problem, because the CSA needs it. I know he's a builder and has two builders who work for him. The whole operation is cash-based, and the CSA tell me they can't do anything about that. They've read his bank statements and they show there's nothing going through, but that's because he puts it all in his girlfriend's accounts. I know where he lives, though.'

'Excellent,' I tell her, relieved we have a lead. 'It sounds simple. First things first. I'd advise surveillance to start off with. We'll follow him from that address to work and compile some evidence about what he's up to. Does he work every day?'

'Oh yes, every day, he leaves between 7am and 9.30am, depending on where he's working.'

'No problem. I'll email you a quote in the next half an hour. You have a think about it, and if you want to go ahead you just have to suggest a day and we'll take it from there,' I tell her, winding up the conversation.

'Wonderful! Oh, thank you so much. I'm so relieved I've found someone who can help! I felt lost with it all.'

Aw, I like this lady! I thank her, get her details and hang up, moving straight on to the quote, which I compile and send through to her. I feel as if the morning has been productive now and decide to wander down to the village shop, pondering this possible new direction for the business.

As soon as I've returned, had some soup for lunch and read the paper, I check my emails. Sarah, the new CSA client lady, has instantly replied and even paid through PayPal! Crikey, she's keen.

Hi Rebecca,

I'd love to go ahead with your services. Any weekday will be fine. I know it's going to be a case of hit and miss, although I am confident he will do exactly as I've said. I can honestly say I'm not bitter, but I know him. He did the exact same thing with his first wife. He didn't want to pay support for the two children he had with her, so he used to do everything in cash and put it through my account. When they got divorced, she ended up with a judgment on him for over £50,000, so now he has even more reason to hide everything he's doing. I suppose this is karma calling, but either way, I need to do something. The whole thing seems so unfair. Anyway, I'll leave it in your very capable hands; just let me know when you have any info.

Best of luck,

Sarah

Oh dear, this certainly seems like karma. Either way, this man is a serial child-maintenance dodger. Who on earth thinks they can have children and not support them? I am infuriated by this man. Hey ho, we've nothing else on for tomorrow, so I'll book it in, and ask Steph to come along with me.

* * *

The alarm shrieks at a terrifying pitch. I've never been a morning person. I hit out to shut it up, but what I really want to do is throw it at a wall. My legs flop over the side of the bed, and I raise my upper half like a zombie. In fact, I probably look like a zombie too – yes, a quick check in the mirror affirms this. Wonderful. I hobble into the bathroom. I'm in my twenties but I'm moving like my grandma. No, maybe not; grandma moves better than I do.

The shower is lukewarm – any warmer and I'd fall asleep standing up! Did I mention it's 5.30am? In my book, when the hands of the clock are anywhere before 7am, it's classed as 'holiday time' – only an acceptable time of day to be awake if you're catching a plane somewhere warm and sunny! But I suppose this is the reality of being a private detective.

I throw on the war paint, going far too heavy on the blusher – but who cares? I'm not supposed to be seen. Hair is just wrong, and it makes me feel stressed, but I need to get over that. Walk out to God's Waiting Room and realise it's a beautiful day. One of the first days of autumn, when you really notice the temperature changing. The leaves are just starting to turn and the sky is bright blue and clear. Ah, I do love God's Waiting Room on days like today. Mrs Timson across the path waves at me as I'm loading up the car: 5.50am and she's up, ready to face the day. What's that all about? I wave back to the happy old dear. She's lovely, really; slightly unhinged – calls me every name but my real one (Sarah, Judith, Joan ...) – and is always up and awake at what I consider crazy times of day, but she's lovely.

Time is moving on and I'm pulling up outside Steph's house. She's equally as prepared as I am: her hair is wet through and she hasn't a scrap of make-up on. 'Wrong, this time of day, wrong!' she moans, getting in the car with a pillow and blanket in tow.

'Morning, Steph.'

'Hello, love,' she says, leaning over for half a hug. 'Where we rocking off to today?' she asks, sticking on a pair of sunglasses like the diva she is.

'Some dude hasn't been paying child maintenance for his kid. Says he's not working but he is. We're off to get the evidence.' I try to stifle a yawn, thinking that as an agency we should just refuse to work before 10am.

'Rock on then, bird.'

'Are you stealing my lines now?'

'Yep, deal with it!'

We've clearly been working together too much lately.

We pull up outside the house where we've been told the target is living with his girlfriend. The new 4x4 he's supposed to drive is parked outside. The estate is rather lovely. Certainly doesn't look as if he's struggling. The house is detached with possibly three bedrooms, and there are neatly kept gardens. A very family-orientated estate – which is ironic considering why we're here. There's a stirring from under the blanket. Steph pops half her head out and lifts her sunglasses only slightly, as if she's a vampire trying to protect herself from the light.

'Arghhhh,' she says, like she's actually in pain. 'Where are we?' She has a puzzled look on her face and I can tell she's going to be highly useful today.

'We're here, and that's his house,' I say, pointing at the brightly painted red door.

'So he's well on the breadline then!' she remarks in her usual sarcastic tone.

'Exactly!' I open a newspaper and sit back while Steph stares out of the window like a puppy looking for its mother. Time to relax. It's 6.45am, which could mean he might not move for the next two and a half hours. We're parked a short distance away, where we have a good view. At first we used to worry that we'd get busybody neighbours and general passers-by coming out to ask who we are and why we're there, but it's never actually happened. This is just another one of the times that prove this job isn't as glamorous as the world might think. After all, Steph has been wakened from the dead, I look like a drag queen and we've both got hair that birds could nest in.

It's 9.25am and Steph is snoring. Not even quiet piggy snores, but loud foghorn ones. I've read the paper three times (even the sports section), picked the varnish off all my nails (fingers and toes), cleaned the car interior with a baby wipe (or ten), played poker, Scrabble, Monopoly and virtual Jenga on my phone, rung my daughter, rung my cousin, rung my nan (I never ring her; must do more often), taken off my make-up and reapplied it (so I look like a normal person) and now I've got my feet on the ceiling, recreating yoga poses. I'm also utterly dying for the toilet – yet another hazard of an investigator's job. I wonder if we should carry potties with us when we're on surveillance work?

Just as the boredom is getting too much to bear, his front door opens. A midget of a man emerges, with a massive head of hair and so much stubble it looks like he hasn't shaved for three weeks. He gets into his car. This is our man! I start the engine so I'm poised and ready to go. He takes off at normal speed (thank you). I wait until he gets round the first corner and ever so slightly out of sight and then … Full throttle! We're off! I feel all my weight pushing back into my seat, and Steph wakes with a start.

'It's murder!' she yells, as she jumps up in her seat and bangs her head on the roof, scaring me half to death.

'What the hell?' I shout.

'I don't know. Is this guy a murderer?' she asks, looking lost. Our abrupt getaway has obviously interrupted a dramatic dream.

'No, stupid! What are you talking about? We're following that 4x4, two cars in front. Keep your eyes open.'

'Sorry, must have nodded off. Maintenance guy, right?' She is perched sideways on the passenger seat, half-resting on the dashboard of the car.

'Yes, Steph. Maintenance guy. Watch him.' Bless her, she looks like a toddler who's just seen the bogeyman!

'On it. He's two cars in front.' Suddenly it feels as though the *Benny Hill* theme tune should be playing in the background. It's a good job our clients don't see us at work or they'd think we were pretty darn incompetent.

There are traffic lights approaching. An investigator's worst nightmare. I once read a private investigation manual that addressed the problem of speeding and traffic lights. In basic terms, it said that whatever you do, don't speed and don't go through traffic lights. Your driving licence is part of your golden investigator's work tools. You need it desperately because without it you simply don't have a business. Well, if any police officers are reading this, I'm sorry … but there are times you can't play by the rules – and when the lights change after the guy you're tailing has gone through is definitely one of them.

'It's RED!' Steph screams. I approach with caution.

'Keep your eyes on him, and only him,' I tell her firmly. There are two lanes, and a car at the side of me. I look carefully, and, holding my breath – I'm even tempted to shut my eyes – I go for it! Yes, I know it's wrong, but I do it very carefully. I promise. OK, I'll go to church tomorrow and say sorry, but if we lose him, the whole morning has been a waste.

'You'll frigging kill me one day,' Steph shrieks.

'Let's hope not,' I say calmly. 'Can you see him?'

'Yes,' she sighs, her relief tinged with disapproval. Next up, we face roadworks. For God's sake! It's just not funny. He is five cars in front, which is a recipe for disaster.

'Can't see him,' Steph tells me.

Wonderful! The traffic comes to a standstill.

'Screw this,' I say.

'What are you doing now?' Steph asks with concern as I pull into the hard shoulder to overtake the traffic on the outside. Yet another illegal move but if I hadn't done it, we'd have lost him because somehow he's managed to get as far as thirteen cars in front. There's a gap in the perfect spot, which I zip into just before he can see us.

'Rebecca, you don't pay me death money!'

'Sorry. No more illegal moves,' I promise with my fingers crossed.

Thankfully, about a mile further down the road the subject pulls into a building site. We slump back in our seats and breathe a sigh of relief. Honestly, I feel as if I've been holding my breath since he emerged from that front door.

'I hate traffic,' I say, reaching for the video camera. Steph is grabbing the stills camera, ready to snap away. The subject goes into one of those horrible Portakabins – made of some kind of metal, and not only plain ugly but also depressing. He emerges wearing a hard hat and a fluorescent jacket.

'What a spoon,' I remark. 'Not working, my foot!'

Steph shakes her head in disapproval.

Our subject proceeds to direct men on the building site, waving his arms to show them where to go and what to do, and we video him for the next hour from behind a wall, and through some side railings.

'Think that's what we call a result,' Steph says.

'Correct. Let's go get something to eat. And have a pee!'

We take off and have lunch. Later on, when Steph has safely been returned to her bed, I review the footage. What we have is the car-camera, which is set up on the front dashboard of the car, showing him leaving for work from his girl-friend's house. I run a search and find she rents it. Also, the film footage and photos of him on the building site show that he's clearly in a position of authority. I throw together my report, based on all the timings and factual evidence, and send it off to Sarah.

'You are absolutely wonderful,' she telephones to tell me, sounding ecstatically happy.

'Aw, you're welcome.' I leave out all the parts about the red lights, hard shoulder and general law-breaking.

'I'm sending it off to the Child Support Agency straight away. I can't thank you enough for what you've done. I knew this is where he was, and what he was up to, but now I actually have the evidence.'

I feel really happy for her and just hope she gets some justice.

*   *   *

Two months go by and to my surprise I see 'Sarah CSA Case' flash on my phone.

'Hi, Rebecca, it's Sarah.'

She must have an update for me.

'I sent off all the evidence to the CSA, and they interviewed my former husband again. He came up with a cock-and-bull story that this was a one-off, and that he isn't in full-time work. He says he got offered a job managing a site for a week, and took it, but now he's unemployed again.'

'Oh dear,' I tell her. 'This is not good.'

'I know. He's so slippery! I'm furious. I know what he's doing, but it's just proving it!'

'It's such a shame that when we get proof he can so easily lie his way out of it.' I feel genuinely disheartened for her.

'There's only one thing for it. I know it's going to cost a lot, but it needs to be done because I'm not letting him get away with this. Can you do exactly what you've already done, but once a week for the next twelve weeks?'

Crikey! 'Of course we can,' I tell her. Thankfully, because he doesn't live too far away, we can have it done in less than three hours each time. The bill's not going to be thousands, but it's still going to be significant.

'Great. Thank you. Send me an invoice and I'll get it sorted for you. Mercifully, my dad's offered to pay!'

That makes me feel a little better, at least. I'd offer to work for her for free, but that's my heart taking over my head again. Mustn't let my personal feelings about dads who don't pay maintenance get in the way of my professionalism! Time to get a grip.

Over the course of the next twelve weeks, we do exactly as Sarah asks. Her ex-husband goes to work from his girl-friend's house every single time. Different building sites, but the same job. We also manage to track down his website, on which he touts his services as an 'independent project manager'. That will do nicely. I print off the pages and send them to Sarah. You can't simply send a web link to the Child Support Agency and ask them to look at it – it's against their rules – so we have to print off each page and send them. The client will get a full package from us that they can submit directly to the CSA – all part of the service!

After the twelve weeks are up, Steph and I catch up over skinny lattes.

'I'm still worried they're going to turn round to Sarah and say it's not enough,' she frets.

'I know what you mean: he could invent an explanation for everything. What else can we do, though?' I sit back, large white mug in hand, staring into the foamy milk for inspiration. Thankfully, it doesn't take long before it dawns on me. 'We sting him!'

'With a bee?' Steph is confused.

'No, silly! We set up a honey trap. But instead of trying to seduce him and seeing if he responds, we lure him to work for us. We pay for his services. He says on his website he's a project manager – so let's find something for him to project manage!'

'Ooooh!' Finally, pennies are dropping all over the place. 'I get it! Nice thinking, brains!'

Smugly, I sit back in my chair and dream up a way in which we can perform this little exercise.

* * *

'Yes, this will do perfectly,' says Steph, whom I'm currently hoisting up so that she can peer over a six-foot-high brick wall.

'Can you see the way in, though?' I ask, getting impatient as her heel digs into my thigh.

'Possibly. Get me down,' she says, brushing the dust from her all-black ensemble. 'Come around this way.' And she walks – no, teeters – in her heels, towards some trees.

We squeeze through a gap between the trees and the wall. Following the path round leads us to an opening at the opposite side, revealing a plot of land with the foundations of a house poking out. It's a Sunday morning, the time of day when the residents of God's Waiting Room will be out in force, wearing their fanciest hats to swan around the village church. All in the name of religion, of course.

'Let me handle this one,' Steph says, digging out her phone from her Louis Vuitton handbag. She looks pleased with herself, and is clearly loving this case, as she dials the number our subject gave on his website. 'Hello, my name is Jennifer Hall. I develop properties. I'm sorry for ringing on a Sunday but we've had a minor emergency. The project manager on one of our properties handed in his notice this morning and is leaving us in the lurch. We need someone to manage our site a.s.a.p, and I found your details on the Internet.'

She's made a good start, but it's a little risky. What if he is fully booked for the next few weeks? Steph clearly didn't think of that possibility, but I'm keeping my fingers crossed.

'Oh really? OK, that should be fine with me. How would it work?'

I rub my hands together to ward off some of the chill in the air. It's sunny but the summer warmth has gone. I hop from one stiletto to the other, realising we are highly inappropriately dressed for the occasion. As always.

'Sorry, I'm going away tomorrow, but we really need some-one to start next week. Is there by any miracle a possibility you can come now?'

I smile a big cheesy grin, still hopping, giving her a thumbs-up!

'Oh, thank you, that would be amazing. Don't worry. If you take the job, you can bill us for Sunday hours,' Steph tells him, joining in my hopping.

The conversation ends. 'He's on his way.'

Exceptionally chuffed with ourselves, we dance through the mud and puddles back to the car.

Some forty-five minutes later and we're in position. We drive round to the site and set up the video camera in the car window. I'll take some snaps from my post in the car.

'You ready?' I ask her.

'Rock and roll ready.'

'Good job. Looks like he's here.'

His 4x4 drives around the corner. Steph opens the car door, and bounces out with her usual cheery attitude.

'Hellooooo! Thanks *sooo* much for coming. I'm sorry for dragging you out today.' She gives him her sparkliest smile. Sat in the car, I hardly hear anything else that's going on. There's lots of nodding and walking around the foundations, but finally they part with a handshake. Somehow she has convinced him she knows about construction!

Steph gets back into the car. 'Drive, quick, round there,' she says, pointing just past the trees. I pull up in a spot where we can still watch him but he won't be able to see us.

'What did he say?' I ask her.

'He said that he's contracted to another job for the next nine months, something he's been working on for over a year. He can't leave his current job, but he has other men on his books who he can employ and manage for us. It will cost around £1,000 per week, because they're specialists or something.'

Steph has a triumphant grin on her face and I'm not only relieved but also exceptionally happy.

'But why's he still there, though?' Steph has a good point. What's he doing now?

'I'm not sure,' I say, shuffling into a position where I can see better. He walks around the site a bit more, poking his nose into an outhouse. Very strange.

'Oh my God!!!!' We both sit there, stunned. 'Is he doing what I think he's doing?'

'I think so,' Steph says, staring in amazement. '*He's stealing the boiler!*'

The dirty-dog of a project manager/child-maintenance dodger/fraudster/outright thief loads the boiler into his 4x4, along with some copper piping, before finally driving off!

The video is pretty good, and Steph writes up a full witness statement about their conversation.

I speak with Sarah once again to tell her what's happened, then send her our full report. The CSA orders her ex to pay maintenance, but still it's not the end of that slippery guy trying as many ways as he possibly can not to pay for his child. He's the type that will always find a way to get out of it. You'd think Sarah would be angry, very angry, but actually she is just sad and disappointed. I'm sure that over time the sadness will pass and the anger will return. Maybe we'll be called back to film him again when that happens. He'd better watch his step ...

THE DATING GAME

Gradually we get more business at The Lady Detective Agency and it begins to seem as though we might actually make a living from it one day. I'm over the moon because – all modesty aside – I think I have a natural talent for it. I'm getting better at asking the right questions on those initial phone calls, and we're gearing up with lots more useful detective gadgets all the time. I've got to admit, some are quite fun, making us feel like female James Bonds, but I've learned you can't rely on them. Technology always fails when you need it the most. It's a bit like phone reception: when you need to call someone, and it's a matter of life or death, you will have no reception. Happens every time!

I like to be a traditional investigator. Hiding behind a computer and a bunch of technology is the cheat's way out. I prefer to feel I've used my brain and done some proper detective work to get results.

Paris and I are splitting our time between living in God's Waiting Room with the parents and in our actual home in the barn. The divorce case isn't getting any prettier, but otherwise life is good and I'm happy. Except that everyone seems to think I should start dating again, so I can look for 'true love'. Pah! What's that when it's at home? Does it even exist? Or is it just a fairy tale invented by marketing types?

You know what I'm hating? Other people's relationships. I'm absolutely sick and tired of them. They argue and bicker all the time, and it's stressful to listen to my friends complaining of this or that about their other halves. Very worryingly, I think I'm becoming a 'relationship basher'. I just have to read the newspaper to see all the horrors of cheating, wife-beating and general lies to wonder – what is the point? Why do people actually get together? When I look around me, I realise I don't know any couples who are truly happy … or at least I don't think they are. Even the friends who are getting married have issues. I think back to my own wedding day, when I knew in my heart of hearts I shouldn't be doing it. What if everyone out there is the same? What if everyone is unhappy? What if relationships are a serious figment of fairy tales? The thought that true love is a total myth is highly disturbing but I've come to the conclusion it's true. I don't think real love between couples exists. There – see? – I said it!

My parents have been married for well over forty years, and I grew up with the ideal scenario. My whole childhood I believed there's one person out there for everyone, that you get married and then live happy ever after. You have babies, a nice house and everything in the world smells of roses. Which is a bit of a daft statement for me to make considering I have no sense of smell. Actually, maybe it's the perfect statement for me to make, because it's all bullshit. The world smells of roses? Bullshit. Relationships are bullshit. I'm much happier on my own.

Let's not forget my job here. It's new and exciting, and that has sort of put a sticking plaster over the deeper problem, I think. The bottom line is that I'm dealing with the ultimate in horror stories of relationships. It's definitely making me more cynical about human nature, but I can't let this job get to me so much that I end up a bitter and twisted old woman who sits in a rocking chair on a veranda rocking all day long with tons of cats miaowing around!

I want to believe in relationships, marriage and all those wonderful things just as much as I wanted to believe in fairies when I was a little girl. The only problem is that no matter how hard I believed, it never worked. I sprinkled myself with cut-up bits of tin foil that doubled up as fairy dust, I tried jumping off the end of my bed to help me fly and I drank all the water in the world because mum told me it had flying dust in it. For about two years, I performed this little ritual every day and I still couldn't fly! Now it's getting much harder to take the leap of faith when it comes to relationships.

But then I think of the cats and the rocking chair scenario. The only way to avoid that, and get myself through my 'relationships are fairy tales' crisis, is to join the dating game. I'll do it with my eyes wide open and bullshit detector on full alert, but I decide I'll give it a try.

Easier said than done. How do you even get started when you work from home and spend most evenings doing childcare? And I seem to have forgotten the rules of the game in the seven years since I was single – or maybe I never knew them in the first place. It's all so flaming awkward. How do you make it clear you like someone without being considered 'easy'? If you blatantly ask someone out, you're seen as cheap. If you say you like something about them, you're labelled a whore. Back in my teens, it seemed to happen a lot more naturally. Now I'm actively looking for someone, it's way more difficult.

A friend signs me up for online dating. After weeding out all the locals who have been knocking around forever I start 'chatting' to one or two guys, but my cynical detective side rears its head straight away. First, I don't trust their pictures. Second, I don't trust they are who they say they are. Third, it's weird. Fourth, it's really weird.

Still, I organise a date with one of them, who comes from over 150 miles away. I'm not sure why he wants to travel so far because it's hard to see how a relationship could work over that distance, but he assures me he wants to and doesn't mind the fact it's only for dinner. He books himself into one of the area's five-star hotels and reserves a table for us at a Michelin-starred restaurant. We've been chatting for about six weeks online, and had a few phone calls, and he seems OK – as far as it's possible to tell.

The day of the date arrives and I'm a bit apprehensive, mainly because I'm apprehensive about meeting anyone for the first time. I keep thinking that I would much rather finish work, pick up Paris from playschool, pop to the supermarket and get something lovely for tea, go home, cook it, bath Paris, do our nightly 'chat to the sheep' session and then have a glass of wine in the bath before going to bed. I pop to the post office and as I'm coming out something hits me – I don't have to go. I know he will virtually be in the area by this point, so how do I tell him I don't want to see him after he's made so much effort?

I don't tell him. I just ignore the phone. When I go to the supermarket, I leave it in the car. When I'm in the bath, I leave it downstairs. Relief floods over me. I don't have to have dinner with him. No one is holding a gun to my head. So much apprehension and nervousness isn't right. Maybe I'm not ready to date after all. I feel like the world's number one bitch but I simply don't go. I just can't face it.

As you can imagine, he doesn't take it well. I apologise profusely, but he's very cross for a few days – rightly so, I suppose. However, it does teach me a valuable lesson: say no to Internet dating. It's not for someone like me who has a suspicious nature. I cancel my membership of the dating site, and that's the end of that little spell. No more trying so hard to make a relationship happen.

In idle moments, though, I find myself browsing around on Facebook. That's something else that's changed in the seven years since I was last dating. It's strange that we're all literally just a click away from anyone we ever knew – well, almost. I check out some of my old boyfriends but all it does is make me feel glad I'm not with them any more. One asks me out, even though I can clearly see he has a girlfriend! I wouldn't have said yes anyway but if alarm bells could sound, blimey would they be screaming!

Bit by bit I'm getting a little more adventurous with my Facebook research – and one day I come upon one of those daft quizzy things. There's a picture of lots of characters, and you have to tag a person on your friends list to the picture. The characters all have a title or meaning, for example:

- The person with the best hair: that went to Jane, a very good friend of mine, whose hair is amazing!
- My best childhood friend: that was Rachael. She was my best friend through five out of the seven primary

school years – and that's a lot by primary school standards.

The questions continue: person with the best smile ... person who makes me happy every day ... Then it comes to the person I had a childhood crush on. So I tag a boy named Ben. I'd been to high school with him, and he was the very first person I remember having a serious crush on. The crush lasted about a year or even two, and was pretty hardcore stuff. As soon as I answer, that little tag sends waves of fear shuddering through me. It's fear of rejection, I guess. By anyone else's standards it's no big deal to tag someone on Facebook, but to me – I can't believe I've had the nerve to do it.

All my friends start adding funny comments about what they've been tagged as, but Ben doesn't. I'd checked out his profile a couple of times when he'd added me as a friend about six months earlier and he has a similar look to the boy I remembered, but has certainly grown up. His relationship status isn't listed, and he doesn't really put any information of substance on his profile. I don't know exactly what to think. I just keep hoping he will reply – but he doesn't.

Two weeks go by, and one morning as I log on I see I have a message in my private inbox.

'Used to have a crush on me, eh? x'

It's Ben! And he's added a kiss! Wow. I'm grinning from ear to ear.

'You didn't know? x' I reply.

'Of course I knew. I also remember our kiss behind the bike sheds! Haha! x'

What? I don't remember a kiss behind the bike sheds. It looks as though he's got me mixed up with someone else. He dated one of my best friends in school for two whole years, but he can't be mixing me up with her, surely?

'Ah, I'm afraid you've got me mixed up with someone else :-(x'

I do remember having a very minor conversation about dating him, at the grand age of thirteen or fourteen. My friend Lauren brokered the conversation, because back in those days you never actually asked someone out yourself. We ended up dating for twenty-four hours, I think it was, and then he dumped me. Nice. That didn't stop my crush, though, and it took a long time to get over it.

'No, it was you alright. I'd remember that kiss any time. x'

Ooooh, is he flirting?

'Haha, you're going to have to enlighten me because I've got no idea. x'

'It was during that spell when we dated for a day. You were wearing your school uniform, with a double-breasted fitted black jacket and black shoes that had a strap across the middle and a really high heel and platform. Remember now? x'

Oh my God. Psycho stalker boy. He's totally right. I remember that outfit well.

'Goodness, you certainly have my attention now. x'

Secretly I am flattered, and a little bit scared.

'I told you I couldn't forget that kiss. x'

Ben goes on to ask what I've been up to, and if I am dating anyone. I tell him that I'm in the middle of a divorce and attempting to get back into dating, but finding it hard. He suggests we should have a little date 'for old times' sake' – and I agree.

We arrange to have lunch the following Wednesday.

I'm working on the Wednesday morning doing some background research for a new client – trying to trace a man who owes a lot of money to their company and has done a runner. Not that I could concentrate very well; the morning passed in a bit of a haze. I'm feeling apprehensive, which in turn is making me feel a little scared. Not scared of seeing Ben, more worried that I'll do what I did last time I arranged a date and stand him up. I'm literally going to have to force myself to go; I'm such a wimp about dating now. Ben lives over an hour and a half away. I offered to meet him at a mutually convenient halfway point, but he insisted on coming to my village. Which was very gentlemanly of him.

I'm sitting in my car waiting for him when he texts to say he's just parked and is walking towards me. Will I remember him? In school he had ultra-blond hair and was really short. He doesn't have many pictures on Facebook, and most were taken in nightclubs so it's hard to make him out. Wonder if that's a bad sign? If there's one thing I do know from my job, people hardly ever look like they do in a Facebook picture. In my head is a picture of the boy from school, not the grown-up version I'm preparing to meet. I don't really like short men, so I am praying he's grown in height. In the distance I see a man walking across the car park. He's tall and well-built, but not stupidly so, like a body builder who can't even walk properly because his muscles are so over-developed. This guy looks an athletic type. He seems like someone you wouldn't mess with. His hair is short, and more dark than blond. I'm still not sure, but when my phone starts to ring and he tells me his exact location, I know it's him. Blimey.

I get out of the car and beam a smile at him, more fake than natural because I am so darn nervous. He gives me a hug and we walk towards the restaurant.

* * *

After about an hour I sit back and assess how it's going. We've had our food and still have not stopped talking. I'm probably talking more than him because I'm so nervous but I'm loving the way he watches me as I speak. He seems almost transfixed, which I hope is a good thing. Unless I've got something stuck in my teeth … His smile is utterly amazing, the type of smile that could power a power station. His accent is broad Lancashire. I've lost most of my accent by this point, because it's become an amalgamation of the various places I've lived since school.

It turns out he's a copper now, which I don't love. I never really liked the police, but that may stem from my issues with authority. I like to be my own authority.

'What made you decide to join the police?' I ask him.

'I didn't really. My mum thought it was a good idea. I wanted to play cricket for a living, but she said I should get a "proper" job. When she got the application forms and wafted them under my nose it seemed a decent idea so I filled them in. I think she wanted me earning enough money to get rid of me! Then when I went through the process and was accepted, it felt right. I was eighteen then, and I've never done any other job.'

Funny thing is, his story – while different from mine – rings very true. I always wanted to be an actress. I wasn't interested in academia, I just wanted to be on a stage, singing and dancing. My parents by rights should have been horrified when I went home and told them that I wanted to study drama at college. They weren't, though. They supported my choice and never tried to change my mind. They still don't try now. In the end I did what I wanted and found my own path. After two years of studying drama, I decided I didn't really like being in front of an audience. I loved entertainment, but wanted to be more behind the scenes. So Ben wanting to play cricket but taking the sensible path instead rang bells with me. Sometimes I wonder what would have happened if I'd done the same. Gone to university perhaps? Studied a normal topic. Truth is, I'm just one of those people who needs to find their own way in life and make their own mistakes. And blimey have I made them!

'I commiserate with you on your career choice,' I tell him, laughing, but half serious. Thankfully he finds it funny. People often think that investigators and the police work closely together, but this couldn't be further from the truth. We never work with them, and I don't think he'd appreciate my occasional need to run red lights. Best to skim over all that!

'I still play cricket though!' he says with a passion.

'Yeah? I know nothing about cricket, I'm afraid. Never watched it, or understood it.'

'Girlfriends in the past have said the same, but it's a huge part of my life. I've never had a girlfriend who supported it.'

I feel sorry for him at this point. He deserves to be supported in something that is such a clear passion for him. I make a conscious decision then and there, that if we start seeing each other I'll try my hardest to understand cricket! I always believe people need to be supported in their passions.

He asks what I do and doesn't seem fazed by it, thankfully. Nor does he ask me a million questions the way some people do, and I'm grateful for that. The 'skim over mission' can continue. Of course, I can't answer certain questions because of client confidentiality and because I don't want to give away our trade secrets – not that he won't have a few of his own.

Ben tells me he saw me a good few years back and tried to talk to me but I blanked him. He says it really gutted him, and at that stage he termed me 'the one that got away'. Highly flattering. I never realised I'd had such an effect. But he'd had me on his Facebook friends list for over six months, so why hadn't he done anything about it before? His answer is interesting and reassuring. He had a girlfriend then, and he's not a cheater. He thinks it would have been wrong even to message another girl when he was in a relationship, so as much as he wanted to, he didn't. He split up with her four weeks ago, then when he saw I'd tagged him on Facebook he thought maybe now was the right time.

I suppose cynical me could do my own little investigation on him to make sure he is telling the truth, but I decide against it. He doesn't seem to be feeding me cheesy lines, or trying to overly impress me. There is something very calming and reassuring about him. I have to base my judgements on individual characters, not deem him a liar on our first date and whip out the ladies to follow him. How can I get to know the real him if I judge and make up my mind beforehand? God help him if I ever think he's lying to me, though!

Our lunch lasts over five hours and by the end of it, I am semi-hooked. I head home with a smile on my face.

DIAMOND-DEALING FAILURE

Monday morning. I'm sitting in my home office with Jess. Winter is on the way, and I couldn't actually be happier. I love this time of year when you can bring out your winter coat and buy some new boots, while looking forward to Christmas. Small things, I guess, but I'm in a pleasant mood. As is Jess, thankfully. It's often not worth the hassle when one of us is in a bad mood. We're far too much alike for our own good. When we have work to do we're great together, but at other times our friendship suffers. Who on earth has a better working relationship than a personal one? I'm not sure that's a good thing.

I'm attempting to fly through the accounts. I hate them, but what self-employed person actually enjoys such a tedious process? Jess, that's who. She likes knowing how much money has or has not been made. This particular morning she's giving me a lecture about our charges. They need to be higher, apparently. Personally I don't care. As long as we're covering our costs and making some money, I'm happy.

Jess is a follower of the original investigator's belief: 'If people are desperate for the service, they will pay almost anything for it.' I know she's right, but it feels morally wrong.

Even though, given the bizarre and crazy work I've had since we opened, over-pricing should be my last worry.

The telephone rings; it's the James Bond theme tune this week, which makes things a little bit more fun as I run and jump over chairs to get to the phone. Makes me feel like I'm starring in a movie.

'Hello?'

The caller identification is withheld. Why did I just answer? I never answer withheld numbers. The voice on the other end sounds ridiculously English and posh. I respond to the person with a clipped, prim and proper English tone, rather far away from my own Northern chimes.

'I have a problem, my dear.' Quite a standard phrase for a new customer – without the 'my dear' on the end!

'Of course. How can I help?' I try to pick up my happy tone because this lady sounds rather dreary.

'I think my husband is being unfaithful with another lady. I need your help.'

Her accent may not be as difficult to make out as a foreign one, but she is extremely posh, and I often wonder if what I hear is the same as the rest of the world. I always struggle to hear words correctly – I'm the classic person who, when you say one thing, I hear another. 'Would you like a pear?' could very easily be 'I don't care'. It leads me into various problems! I had an interview once, for a 999 advisor role. They put me through test after test after test. One of the tests was to listen to a distressed 999 caller, and answer questions based on the information they had given me. I failed. It was the one area throughout the whole of the day that I failed, and ultimately the reason I didn't get the job. Reason being, I don't listen. My dad held that story against me for months – 'Rebecca doesn't listen' … Listening to this woman I feel like I'm back in that interview.

After a little while I decipher the brief. The woman, Flo, is from Surrey and her husband the same. He is a diamond dealer. To be honest, when she told me that I really thought I was being set up. It took all my strength not to say 'Yeah, right' and then hang up. But there was an air of honesty in her posh voice.

There's something different about her. She seems guarded about what she's telling me, only giving the bare facts and leaving out her emotions. My clients are almost always in emotional and distressed states. Flo isn't. I can't tell if it's because she's been brought up sporting a stiff upper lip, if she honestly doesn't care or if that's just the type of woman she is. There's no point in trying to crack her shell: if she wants to work this way, fine by me. I get attached to a lot of my clients and truly empathise with their stories, mainly because they give it to me warts and all. This could be a refreshing change. 'Professional and classy' is the best way to describe this lady.

Her husband is called Edwin, and he is exceptionally wealthy. Flo thinks he is keeping a secret mistress. Over a year ago she discovered he'd been leading a double life online. He used discreet websites catering to a certain market – people who are married but want to have an affair. Apparently he'd been a member for over a year by the time Flo made her discovery. From that point on, Flo embarked on her own DIY detective spell.

Listening to her call, I can't help but feel stressed. I'd once been there myself, but now I was on the opposite side I knew how dangerous it can be. In my now-professional capacity I know it mucks up our work too. Eventually, DIY detectives always get found out by their other halves.

Problems for the professionals occur when the DIY version struggles. They will eventually come up against a challenge too difficult for them to cope with, and try to hire us. All very well and good, but by now their partner knows they have the intention to snoop. We have to be even more cautious than we'd have had to be in the first instance. If only the person had hired us as soon as they had suspicions, before any obvious cracks were appearing in the investigation! We need to come totally out of the blue, and never be suspected, let alone caught. It makes life so much simpler for us.

Back to the conversation, and Flo tells us the details of her DIY detective mission. To be fair to her, she didn't do a bad job – I've certainly heard worse. It turned out he had been paying for his mistress to set up a new business, and even for her brand new apartment. He wasn't the most cautious of men, paying for gifts for her out of their joint account. Who does that? It was all she had found out, but it was enough for her. Flo confronted him, and the secret affair was over, apparently. Now we've fast-forwarded a year and there are new suspicions. What exactly these are she never says. I ask on a couple of occasions, but she dances around the topic and moves on. It feels as though she doesn't have any real foundation for her latest worries, but wants to check anyway. Either way, it's not my place to probe her, so I don't. With Flo I make sure our interactions are nothing but professional, and get straight to the point – how we can help.

Edwin is coming to London on his way back from Dubai. It's only for two days, but we have to monitor him at all times. Flo informs me that he is due at a meeting on the Monday, and that's his main reason for the trip. He also has an invitation on the Sunday evening to an exclusive party with some Russian co-workers. Flo's sure he'll be unfaithful at some point, but she's not sure exactly when. Either way our mission is simple, or so it seems. I tell her I'll plan the job and call her back with a total price. She thanks me and hangs up. I turn and explain the situation to Jess.

'Well then, we're putting *this* price up!' Her logic is simple: 'The woman has a husband who plays with diamonds for a living! She's not short of cash.' Jess has a point, but either way I'm not listening because I soon discover that this little exercise is going to be costly enough without me adding extras.

Flo has told me which hotel Edwin is going to stay in, and there's no way round it – we have to be in the same place. Entering the name into a search engine, we discover that this is no normal hotel. It is one of the best London has to offer: five stars and a special award to boot. It was designed by a super-designer, the best in their field, and some of the greatest people in the world have stayed there. Oh, and it has a Michelin-starred chef. I think we'll be able to cope for a couple of nights there – and at £500 per night for a basic room, it had better be good.

Next is the small issue of the party. If he goes, we need to get in, which is going to be difficult. There's the option of dressing up as waiting staff and filtering in through a back door, but that's a boring idea. We need tickets. Again, my good friend the Internet search engine comes in handy. As suspected, the party proves to be highly exclusive. Now is the time for my years of drama studies to come in useful. I pick up the phone, and ring the organisers. I have no idea where the sudden rush of confidence comes from. Usually I don't do anything like this without serious research, planning and time to compose myself. This time I'm throwing caution to the wind, putting on my very best posh accent and winging it.

'Good morning. I'm telephoning from De Jane Enterprises. I'm sure you must have heard of us. It's regarding your "Entitlement Party".' That's the name of the event, and I'm clearly talking to a very serious Russian woman. Once again, I'm cursing my problem with making out accents.

'How ken I help?'

'I simply need to be in attendance. How can you make this possible?' I ask her.

'I am afraid zis iz not possibul. Zis event iz highly booked up and ze regista process vill tek too long now.' Snooty cow!

'Young lady, I appreciate it is late in the day. I was due in Dubai with Sir Charles Tomlinson on the day of the party, only there's been a small hitch and I am now available to attend. Your associates at Taylors of London [an élite networking group I knew they worked with] highly recommend that I attend this event. I'm sure they will vouch for my credibility, or indeed you can speak with Sir Charles. Either way, I need to attend, regardless of cost.'

The utter rubbish flowing out of my mouth is ridiculous. Jess looks at me in amazement and mutters under her breath, 'You have lost your effing mind.'

'I vill hev to consult vith my employer and zee vat I ken do,' snooty Russian bird tells me.

'Thank you kindly. Would you care for my email address? I shall be on a flight to New York within the next couple of hours and shall be difficult to contact.'

Russian bird takes my email address and the conversation ends. I sit back in my chair and want to collapse with exhaustion. I know I spend a lot of time winging situations, but that was outright silly. There was no chance she would reply, so posing as waiting staff may turn out to be our best option after all.

Just as I'm filing the estimate to Flo, my email notification sounds. It may not be very ladylike, or very good etiquette, but I have a mail alert system that makes flatulence noises. In my defence, I have a good reason. When I load my computer in the morning, I've generally received over thirty emails during the night, and I always wake up grumpy. Hearing my computer constantly trumping for two minutes makes me smile.

Anyway, it's the Russian bird. Apparently her boss has approved our attendance and has fitted us on a table with a diamond seller – but at a cost of £2,500 per ticket. Sipping my coffee I almost choke, and then fall about laughing. Who actually attends these things? Either way, I put it in my estimate to Flo. She'll then be able to decide how important it is for us to be there. The bill is ridiculous. Our fees are minimal in comparison to the expenses.

The telephone rings within five minutes of the invoice being sent. It's Flo, informing me that my costing is absolutely fine and yes, she wants us at the party. Her friend will call me in twenty-four hours to pay, because she's scared of being caught if she does it herself. I reassure her that any card payments to the agency will show up as being to a clothing company, so no one will get suspicious. Just one of the many little details we had to think of when setting up the agency.

★   ★   ★

It's the next day, and I'm driving down the motorway when the phone rings. I answer it, hands-free of course.

'Hello daaarling, this is Ingrid. Friend of Flo's.' We exchange pleasantries; her friend seems bizarre but nice. She pays with her card over the phone, and the details are taken by Jess, who's in the car with me listening to the conversation while I'm still driving. And then comes the real bombshell.

'Do you have other services?' Flo's friend asks.

'Oh yes, we do almost everything. What are you thinking of?' I ask, as I indicate and change lanes.

'Do you kill the cheating bastards too, darling?' My eyes almost pop out of my head, and Jess and I look at each other with serious alarm. Has she just asked if we kill the cheating bastards? I clearly haven't misheard, or Jess would not have had the same reaction. I try to laugh it off.

'No, no, no, we don't offer those kinds of services … ha ha ha!'

'Oh, really? Why ever not? You could make a lot of money.' WHHHAT is this woman saying? Is she being serious? She's laughing, but there are some things that you just don't say!

'No, we just catch them, I'm afraid. We would never get involved in that kind of thing.' Now I'm starting to get scared.

'I was only joking, darling,' she says, and I realise it was her super-posh accent that made me think otherwise! Normality is restored, and Jess and I are highly relieved.

I speak with Flo twice more before the job. I have pictures of her husband, descriptions of the clothes he's had packed by their maid (crikey!) and every tiny piece of information she knows about what he will be doing.

*   *   *

In the run-up to this job I had been really ill. I could barely speak, my nose was streaming and I kept wanting to be sick. The first reality of being your own boss dawns when you realise there's no one to take over if you're sick. I'm still a bit under the weather at 3am on the morning we're due to head for London. The alarm clock is going off at a time when the younger version of me would only just have been going to bed after a fun night of partying. Forget make-up and hair. I throw the suitcase in the car just as Jess is pulling up on the drive. She looks as rough as I do. We hardly say two words to each other as we set off for the Big Smoke. This might be a fun and exciting job, but at this time of the morning, feeling as ill as I do, I couldn't care less.

It takes all of three hours and a small glimmer of the sun coming up above the horizon before either of us is remotely sociable, and when we are, the service station is our next stop. Coffee and muffins follow, as do make-up and some effort with the unruly hair I'm sporting. Just in case we don't get another opportunity to stop, we arm ourselves with equipment. We feed body cameras through our tops, and don radio devices which go from our sleeve through to an ear piece. All so we can speak to each other without being noticed. Usually we don't bother with radios, because it's all a bit dramatic – and besides, the technology almost always fails just when you need it most. On this occasion, however, we can't be on our phones every ten seconds, texting and talking, so a more covert operation is necessary.

The forthcoming mission is to find Edwin. He's arriving on the 10.30am flight into Heathrow. Thankfully we arrive early, and plan our positions. The car parking is a nightmare. There are three options: Edwin will go up to the top floor and collect a rental car, go to the front of the building and get in a taxi, or go through the back entrance to a different taxi rank. Jess opts to stay with our car, but the airport security guards are being irritating. We're only allowed to stay in the pick-up zone for five minutes, and they are already on our backs after two. There's no option but to park in the multi-storey and hover in the car around the exit barrier. What that means is that I will have to radio over to Jess when Edwin is coming out of the terminal, then she'll pay the ticket, jump back in the car and exit. Simple.

Around the corner in the McDonald's car park I dive into the boot to retrieve a wig, since it would raise too much suspicion if I was spotted at the terminal and then at the hotel. Now, my boot is nicknamed Narnia by the girls because it contains every kind of disguise you can imagine: changes of clothing, wigs, specs, make-up – you name it, I've got it. Of course it's a bit messy but that can't be helped. Two teenage boys are parked up in the car next to us. Their faces look as horrified as the man who saw Mrs Doubtfire change from a man to a woman. I smile and wave, and they very quickly go back to eating their burgers, highly embarrassed. Dressed in jeans, flip-flops, a vest top, glasses and a blonde wig, I'm ready to go.

Jess drives the car around to the front of the terminal, drops me off and takes her place in the multi-storey. I swiftly move inside the terminal and sit on a chair. One that's not directly in eyeshot of the arriving flight passengers. The arrivals boards are updating, but not telling me what I want to see – turns out the flight he's on is delayed by twenty minutes. I radio back to Jess, but keep watching everyone who is coming through the gate. I check the boards every minute, and they still say the same.

Hundreds of people are coming through – three flights have landed all at once and it's crazy. The board is still showing the plane as delayed, but then it changes in a flash to saying that the flight landed thirty minutes ago. Sheer horror shoots through me. I'd checked everyone who'd come through, and no one matched the pictures. Then I spot a man who's the spitting image of Edwin – he fits the description perfectly. It's him. I radio through to Jess, who pays for the ticket and moves towards the exit barrier of the car park. I'm following on foot, and Edwin is in front of me. He goes to stand on the island near the car park, which is the place to wait if someone is picking you up. As I turn the corner to get in the car, Jess is still at the exit barrier. Something isn't right.

'This stupid bloody thing has swallowed the ticket and won't let me out!' Jess is screaming at the machine. The shit is hitting the fan. 'Someone is on the way,' she tells me.

It is highly possible we'll lose Edwin. I dive straight back out of the car and hurry over to the island to make sure we keep him in sight. A car pulls up alongside him. The ticket agent who's come to fix the machine is nothing short of a dithering old fool. He isn't letting us go without checking the ticket, making sure we've paid. I try to get back in the car, but Edwin is just out of sight. Now we are both in a panic, but Dithering Fool doesn't care. Edwin has finished putting his bags in the back of the car and is setting off. Quickly I video the car, and memorise the number plate. I bounce back into our car a final time, and Dithering Fool is about to let us out. By now Edwin's car has been out of sight for two minutes. In this game, two minutes is a lifetime. He could be anywhere.

Jess blazes the car out of the car park and past arrivals. We get a few looks as we zoom past, and it's a good job there are

no police around. We have no option. At all times, you have
to do whatever it takes to get the job done. Sadly, it's the
reason why some of us have some points on our driving
licences – me included. As we fly at high speed onto the dual
carriageway Edwin's car mercifully comes into sight, and we
can both breathe again. Staying a couple of cars behind at all
times, we follow for nearly an hour. Instead of going into
London, it looks like he's bypassing it and heading towards
Kent. Could he be aiming for the Channel Tunnel?

'How sure are you it's him, Rebecca?' asks Jess.

'Er, 90 per cent,' I tell her. Another fifteen minutes later it
is down to 80 per cent, and after a further ten minutes … 'I'm
not sure at all any more.'

'Shit,' Jess says, revving up the speed and pulling alongside
Edwin's car. 'That's NOT him!' she says. I'm mortified. Never
before have I failed on such a spectacular scale. I've heard of
incidents like this happening to other detectives, but not us.
Certainly not me!

'Turn around,' I tell her. 'Head to the hotel.' We both sit in
complete silence until we pull up at the hotel. Now Flo's
friend is ringing. I don't know what to do, or what to say. I
can't possibly tell her the truth that we've lost him. Somehow
I have to salvage the situation.

'Hello? How is it going daaarling?' It's Flo's friend all right.

I want to cry! 'Fine, fine, no problems at the moment. Has
he spoken to either of you?' I ask, praying for a clue.

'Yes, he has. Is it fun following him around the food court?'

It's a small clue, but at the moment it feels like a massive
one!

'I mean they do have some excellent specialities, but the
prices are phenomenal. Mind you, if I know Edwin like I

think I do, he'll certainly be splashing some cash on the finer things. Speaking of which, I could kick myself. I needed a certain brand of caviar for my luncheon with the ladies on Thursday – it's only sold in Harrods. If he won't pick some up for me, you ladies could do it couldn't you?'

Bingo! Clue is given. Her request is utterly barking, and she's just told us way too much information, but it's a miracle right now. Thank you, Ingrid! Thumbs-up to Jess.

'If he won't pick some up for you, we certainly shall,' I tell her breezily.

Ingrid finishes off, telling me she has to go and will call again later. After all our dreadful luck earlier in the day, the gods are shining on us!

'Let's dump the bags and wait here,' I say to Jess. He isn't up to anything at the moment, and by our calculations he hasn't had time to change. Surely he will be getting changed before the party?

We walk in through the classic townhouse door of the hotel and into the most beautiful reception I've ever seen. It's huge! Marble covers the floor and walls. There's a fire roaring away at one side, the full length of a very long wall. Surrounding the fire are plush seats made of the softest beige leather, sunk into the marble floor. It certainly has a minimalist feel, but it's beautiful. There's no natural light in the reception; instead, candles are flickering everywhere, creating a supremely inti-mate atmosphere when outside it's blazing daylight. Either way, we approve. The check-in staff are lovely, and we're shown to our room. It has a similar feel to the reception. All the furniture is either covered with white fabric or made of wood. Two double doors lead out onto a balcony that overlooks the London rooftops. We're happy, but there's a job to do.

No sooner have we landed in our room than we turn round and go straight back to reception, taking a laptop, charger, magazines and books with us. We simply are not moving until Edwin surfaces from his shopping trip. We plant ourselves firmly on the sofas in front of the fire, where we have a great view of the hotel entrance. There's no way he can come in without passing us. We're sitting slightly off to a corner, and out of eyeline, just in case.

After an hour we order food from the Michelin-starred chef himself. I have a smoked salmon concoction and Jess chooses something involving beef. Both dishes are served up with the kind of crisps that aren't really crisps – you know, the type that hurt your teeth to bite they're so hard. Someone somewhere thinks they're posh. Personally I'd go for Doritos any day!

While I'm taking one very large bite – because I don't mess around – of my salmon sandwich, Edwin walks through the hotel door behind me, and straight to reception. Jess coughs, and gestures with her eyes. Startled, I stop eating and slope off to the bathroom as Jess sits and watches his moves. At this early stage it's important we're not seen together.

Thankfully we have devices on us that magnify sound. Even though we're some distance from him, we can still hear his quiet conversation with the receptionist. Edwin had gone straight from the airport to do some shopping, and hasn't even checked in yet. We know this because the receptionist asks how his day has been, and what he has been doing. Thank goodness for customer service. He tells her he's done some light shopping, stopped for a bite to eat and now he's here. He also has Harrods bags in his hands. The relief is immense. The earlier drama is becoming a memory – a memory that is fading but still makes me feel a little bit sick.

'Room number 512, sir,' the receptionist informs him. Thank you very much; our lives just got a whole lot easier. With that, he goes to his room.

We return to our spot, and resume eating. Two hours go by, and then three. The reception staff are becoming interested in us. One comes over and asks if she can get us anything. No one else is in the reception, so I can understand why we look a little suspicious. Four hours, and then five … The next staff member to approach asks if we like the reception. Is this idiot having a laugh with us? We'd spent hours sitting in the same spot! Stupid question – he's clearly fishing for more information.

'He thinks we're hookers,' Jess says through gritted teeth, waving her hand to dismiss the staff member. It is now 6.30pm, and the party's at 7.30pm. We have been sitting in the same place for seven hours. Boredom has kicked in. Facebook and Twitter have been checked a thousand times, my face is burning from the stupid beautiful fire, magazines are all read and three chapters of my book are over. We need to change for the party. First Jess goes upstairs, and returns in a floor-length black gown, complete with black high heels. Next I go up while she stays on guard. We don't have time for hair and make-up – we simply have to touch up. I return in a nude-coloured gown with a corseted waist and a borrowed diamond choker.

We decide the next phase of the mission needs to be completed separately. One of us will sit in the car, the other in the reception. All very important to ensure when he does move, we are ready to follow. I take the first car shift and sit out there in the dark on a regal London street, bathed in the light of the street lamp, alongside a classic, enclosed public garden, with townhouses lining the other side of the road. I start to read my book, phone volume turned up ready for Jess's signal to move, but my thoughts keep straying to Ben. It's a week since our marathon five-hour lunch and we've spoken several times and are making plans to see each other again – which makes me feel terrified and excited at the same time.

The lunch was easy and calm, but now after not seeing him for a while the nervous butterflies have returned. Not only that but somewhere along the crazy path I've agreed to cook dinner for him! What's that all about? I'm not exactly a domestic goddess. We seemed to get along so well last time, and we literally didn't stop talking. The idea of going out somewhere or to the cinema didn't really appeal so I suggested a date at home, and he thought it was a perfect idea. That's when he dropped a hint – that he really should sample my 'cooking'. I'd have seen him sooner if it wasn't for this job taking me away. For now, though, I'm just going to have to wait and sit here stewing in my own nervous energy, hoping that when the time comes I don't poison him.

Thirty minutes go by, and Jess comes to take my place. I return to the reception. We swap again, and again, and again. Is Edwin going to go to the party? Doubts are creeping in. We have installed a video camera on his floor, aimed at his room. He hasn't come out, and no one has gone in. At 9.30pm we are having doubts. At £2,500 per ticket, you aren't late on purpose. Or are you?

We keep up the charade for the next two hours, and at last he surfaces. He is wearing jeans and a jacket – not exactly party-wear. This is certainly bizarre. Jess radios me in the car to tell me he's leaving, and he does. He is on foot. I dive into my boot of tricks and put on a long black coat, short black wig and flat shoes. I follow on foot, and leave the keys in the car engine, ready for Jess to take over. He walks over two miles to an all-night shop, where he buys a newspaper and some biscuits. Clearly he wants a stroll and nothing more. He goes back to the hotel, up to his room and that's it. He has opted not to go to the party, and our poor client has forked out £5,000 for tickets. We don't even get to go!

Upon our return, the receptionist collars Jess and me. After spending around eleven hours in one spot, all we want to do is go to bed. The alarm is set for 6.30am, just in case he's an early riser. Early mornings aren't my forte, so I'm not entirely thrilled about it, but needs must.

'Ladies, we would like to offer you something.' We're feeling very sleep-deprived having been awake since 3am the previous morning, and this seems an odd conversation to be having. 'Let me show you. This way,' the receptionist says, taking us to the lift and up to the third floor. Part of me wonders if we are being kidnapped.

'Management would like to upgrade your room,' she says, showing us into a new bedroom. Only 'bedroom' turns out to be the wrong word. We go through the door and into a private lounge with vaulted ceilings, a TV with every movie channel possible, a free mini-bar, an extra-large bedroom with a balcony out onto our own private courtyard, and, in the bathroom, a bath that you have to climb five steps to get into.

'Wow, thank you,' we both reply, feeling very pleased with ourselves. We transfer our bags and settle into our new room. It takes all of five seconds from when Jess goes to the bathroom to have a shower for me to fall asleep. It has been a long and ultimately boring day.

Upon waking at 6.30am we dress and apply make-up as quickly as possible, then go back to our positions in the reception. I ring Flo to inform her of the night's events. She seems relieved, though it's difficult to tell, and says that once he is at his meeting we can go home. Last night had been his perfect opportunity, and he'd done nothing.

Sitting back in the reception I tell Jess of Flo's instructions. We order breakfast – but it's no ordinary breakfast. I've never seen anything quite like it. We are sent two trays each, bearing meats, cheese, pastries, toast, jam, coffee, tea, hot chocolate, full English, scrambled eggs and smoked salmon, poached eggs, eggs Benedict, champagne, berries and all kinds of fruit. Instead of asking what we wanted from the menu, they have simply brought everything. We look at each other and smile. The most ironic part of all this is that there is a man in this hotel who has no idea who we are, and yet he is paying for everything – including the very handsome price of £75 per head just for our breakfast. Thank you, Edwin!

Edwin comes down and sits in the restaurant. He wanders around in the reception, and checks out the library. Gets in a car, and goes to his meeting. And that's it.

★   ★   ★

Our time is over. He has done nothing, and our client has incurred serious expense to find that out. We're booked in for another night, but Flo doesn't want any more information, so instead we hop off to Harrods and have lunch, pore over Louis Vuitton handbags and check out all the beautiful Kensington boutiques. That evening we keep bumping into Edwin in the hotel, and can tell he is genuinely on his own.

Next morning we check out of the hotel. The bill is simply huge for a very short two-night stay, far greater than most average people's monthly salary. Jess asks one question of the receptionist: 'Why did you upgrade our room?'

She looks up at us and smiles. 'You are journalists, are you not?'

'Journalists, ah! We've been caught!' Jess answers, both of us grinning at each other.

With that our London fun is over, and we return to the North. I catch up with Flo soon after. By the end of a case I usually feel like I've got to know the client, but Flo still feels purely like a client. I expected her to be either overwhelmingly happy that she got a good result, or even slightly distressed that we'd not found anything, but she is neither. I thought when I gave her the results that I could sense relief in her voice, but she has kept up the barriers the whole way through her case. Her friend is the total opposite, of course, but Flo doesn't want anyone to see that she's in a personal dilemma. There has been no point before, during or since this investigation when I've felt like I broke her shell. What she truly feels about the results we've given her, I don't think I'll ever know.

There are two types of client in my experience: the ones who tell you their life story thirty times over and the ones who tell you nothing. At first, I liked that Flo was professional and stuck to the facts, but part of me wishes I'd been allowed to get closer to her. It does make me wonder if it's somewhere I went wrong, or if that's just the way she is.

★   ★   ★

A couple of days after we get back from London I find myself standing at my range cooker. It's my second date with Ben. Somehow a pan of vegetables has found its way onto the stove, there's a big frying pan ready for some extra-large steaks and creamy dauphinoise potatoes have miraculously turned up in the oven. OK, so I didn't make the potatoes. They were bought pre-prepared from the supermarket! Either way, I'm not entirely sure how I've ended up in this position. I'm winging it, but for now it's working.

Ben texts to say he's on his way, and the nervous scary butterflies that have invaded my tummy start fluttering like mad.

It doesn't take Ben long before he settles in as if it's his own home. He sits on the sofa casually chatting away about what he's been doing and the sport he's been playing, while I'm in the kitchen busy impersonating a cross between Delia and Nigella. As the conversation continues I find myself drifting through to the sofa, staring at him as he talks and thinking how much I love his eyes. So much so, in fact, that he has to alert me to a burning smell coming from the range! Those potatoes were stupid anyway. I crack open a bag of frozen chips instead and fortunately Ben thinks it's funny and cute – thank goodness for that!

Paris is staying with my mum and dad for the evening. I've already mentioned her to Ben, but feel I need to probe further.

'Have you ever had a relationship with someone who had children?'

'Funnily enough, never!'

I don't know if this is a good or bad thing. It's not easy dating someone who has kids. 'It can be difficult,' I tell him. 'You're not their parent, so you never know if you're doing the right thing. Not to mention the fact they may not even like you.' Am I trying to scare him off already?

'I understand that. I don't expect it to be easy, but I think I can handle it. I'd see it as a fun new little person to get to know. Besides, I'm a big kid myself!' I think it's lovely he has such a rose-tinted view, but equally I wonder if he just doesn't really understand.

Ben doesn't seem sheltered exactly, but he's certainly untarnished. It's either going to be a good thing that he's got no preconceived notions, or a really bad thing because he just has no idea.

Looking at him smiling back, though, I know I've just got to get with it and hope for the best. I want to believe him, have faith and for it to work – and it's only date two! Scary times.

MORALS FLY OUT OF
THE WINDOW

On our website and promotional flyers, we've always claimed to do 'honey trapping online'. I think a lot of people know all about conventional honey trapping, where a girl chats up a man to see if he'll take the bait, but honey trapping online is a new concept.

I can't remember whose bright idea that was, but back in the beginning we set up lots of fake profiles. Facebook, Twitter, LinkedIn and a few online dating sites. We created men, women and businesses. We made them look authentic by putting up pictures. We worked on them, starting up a profile and keeping it going. Leaving it without any activity would look suspicious and wouldn't get us anywhere. Our fake people needed to post messages and have fake lives. It was all very time-consuming, but we knew it would be worthwhile when the time came. We'd already used some of our Facebook profiles for that first job with Jane and the girl at her husband's work, but so far no one had taken us up on the online honey trapping service. You can imagine my surprise when, a little bit like buses, two honey trap jobs came along at once.

★　　★　　★

It's 11pm. I'm tucked up on the sofa watching another re-run of a really rubbishy American programme, with white fluffy slippers, fluffy dressing gown and cocoa in hand when the first of a few texts comes through:

'Hi. I need some help. I think I want my fiancé honey trapped online. Can you help? Jenny.'

'Of course we can, Jenny. Do you want to email us the details and we can give you a quote?'

'That's great, thank you. Sorry for contacting so late at night.'

'Don't worry – nature of the job – I'm just glad you're not asking me to go and follow someone right now :-)'

'Ha ha! That's true. I'll send you over all the info tomorrow to the email address on your website. Thank you.'

Well, she seems nice. Cocoa time is over and I can go to bed a content girl, knowing we have a new job coming in.

It's morning, 10am, which for the residents of God's Waiting Room is pretty much lunchtime. The estate has a drama going on – not just a small drama but a major one. Four residents are currently out on the front street investigating, as I survey the situation from the master bedroom window. There's a police car! I kid you not, a police car in God's Waiting Room! Potentially this could be a murder, or something equally serious. Wait until the vicar hears! He'll be round in a flash. I'm debating going outside when I hear the computer making flatulence noises again. My emails are coming through. I wonder if I should deal with them, or deal with the major situation? I'll deal with the situation.

I wander outside in my fluffy slippers and see the next-door neighbour.

'Arthur, what's happening?' I ask him.

'Well, Rebecca, we don't really know. We're waiting to find out. Maybe the police could use your services?'

'I don't think they'd appreciate my input, Arthur!'

'Mrs Timberly has gone over to ask if she can help out, but I don't think they'll appreciate that either!'

'Let me know what happens. I need to go and get some work done.'

'Right you are, Miss Rebecca.' I love Arthur. He's a chilled-out, old-fashioned kinda guy with respect for everyone. Probably could pass for Santa Claus if we gave him a red outfit.

The police go back to their car and word spreads that it was a case of mistaken identity. Typical! Like I said, nothing ever actually happens round here. I walk back into the house and the computer has finally silenced itself. Sure enough, the email from last night's lady is waiting.

Hi,

I'm sure my fiancé is being unfaithful. He's so flirty with everyone he speaks to. I've simply had enough. I don't want to stay with him, and I need to use it as an excuse to get out. I know that could sound really silly and cold, but I think it would be the best way. I understand if you don't want to take my case on, I know it could be a bit daft, but this keeps niggling me and I need to give it a go.

Thanks,

Jenny

Well, it's certainly different. Do I care? Nope. If she thinks it's going to help then who the heck am I to judge her? If only I had honey trapped James before we got married, I might not have gone through with it and I'd have been spared all that heartache. At The Lady Detective Agency, we're not here to judge people, we're here to provide a service. So let's crack on and see what we can do for Jenny.

Hi Jenny,

Of course we will take your case on. It's not our place to judge you, and we've heard far stranger things. We can get right on with applying a honey trap online to your fiancé. I just need you to send me his details and links to his Facebook page, and we can go from there. The cost is a one-off fee, and you'll find the rates on our website. Essentially we'll carry on with the honey trap and rapport-building until you tell us to stop. If you have any further questions, please feel free to send them over to me.

Many thanks,

Rebecca

We send a couple of emails back and forth, but at the end of it she decides to go ahead and sends us the links to her fiancé. I check him out ... He's not the worst I've seen! That's a relief. He is stocky, tall and has dark hair. He has a strange mouth, and when he smiles his face looks harsh. After a couple of days, during which we randomly add some of his friends on one of our fake Facebook pages, he finally accepts our friend request.

Sitting in the office, I go through his profile with a fine-toothed comb. I trace back from when he first joined Facebook in 2007 and read absolutely everything. It takes me a grand total of three hours and four cups of coffee. There's absolutely nothing of any interest – well, I tell a small lie. The part I do find interesting, and which makes me a little suspicious, is that there are no women whatsoever who have posted on his wall. It's only men. Often when people have something to hide they go over the top to cover up. A man with over 300 friends on the social networking site, yet in four years he has not had one woman post on his wall? He doesn't seem very shy. With all the men who've posted to him he's been chatty, responsive and a bit funny at times. He's no timid shrinking violet. I mean, on the face of it, if he was any more squeaky clean I would be able to smell the bleach from 200 miles away. I find it odd, and it makes me suspicious that he has something to hide.

I start to go through all his pictures and albums. Another hour goes by, as well as another coffee. Usually I'm not quite this thorough. I can sum people up reasonably quickly, but it's pure interest that's making me trawl through the hundreds of photos and posts. I even feel a little disturbed because they have a daughter who looks exactly the same as Paris! To the outside world, they would appear a normal, nice family. On the inside, though, there are serious problems.

It's amazing when you look around at people in the street, or even people you know, and realise that you never know what's actually going on behind closed doors. It makes me question human nature and everything we do. The client must think that this will help her, but potentially I could be about to rip a relationship apart where there's a child involved. Surely no one would come to us who didn't already have serious problems? If they were living a happy, normal life together she wouldn't want us to do this. The resemblance of their daughter to my own makes it very real, and it's feeling a little too close to home right now. I've told my client I'm not judging her, but deep down maybe part of me is. I hate myself for that. I press 'Message' on his profile, and type …

'Hey, let me see if you recognise me??'

I then sit back in my chair with tears in my eyes. What am I doing? Is it right to be an agent provocateur and risk taking a little girl's daddy away from her?

I walk downstairs, and stand in the hallway. The sun is beaming through the glass door, but I just stay still and listen to the silence around me. I look at the table, and open the drawer to get my car keys, walk outside the house into the sun and drive to pick up Paris from playschool. I don't care that I'm picking her up early. I want to spend some time with my little angel. All this work is getting too much. I've pushed it to the back of my mind, but while we've been setting up the business she's been spending too much time with my parents. I can't believe how just one job – not even an especially significant one – has made me so emotional. I start to think about everything Paris has been through, with all the upset and drama. Mostly all she's done the whole time is be happy and smile at me, but sometimes you see her real feelings come out. I haven't introduced her to Ben yet. I need to see what's going to happen first. She doesn't need any more big changes in her young life.

The Lady Detective Agency has been a whirlwind since it started, and she's certainly been along for the ride but I've not made enough time for her. So right now, I'm having some time with her, just my little girl and me.

I walk into her class and she's sitting on the carpet with the other twenty children, all legs crossed listening intently to a story the teacher is telling them. Paris turns her head and sees me standing in the doorway.

'Mummy!' she beams, and looks to the teacher for approval. The teacher nods her head and Paris jumps up and runs over to me, clinging to my leg.

'Sorry. I forgot she has to visit the dentist,' I tell the teacher. Lie. I wonder how many dentist appointments are authentic? It's like the generic excuse when you want to get your kid out of school. I've only pulled her out an hour early, so I don't feel too guilty. Besides, it's only playschool. The teacher smiles, and tells Paris she'll see her tomorrow. The angel goes to her book drawer and gets her coat from her peg. I watch her doing her normal everyday things and it fills me with love and happiness.

Walking through the park and playing with Paris on the swings and slides makes the sadness slowly vanish. I'm not sure if it's just this job that's bothering me, or our whole business. The things we do cross so many moral boundaries. In answer to the critics, I say that we're not here to judge, and that we truly do help people in a very strange way. But I don't think I'd be human if I didn't occasionally question myself and what we do. After all, I don't ever forget that although my exterior is pretty hard, and sometimes calculating, underneath I'm emotionally as weak as a kitten.

We spend the rest of our day back home with lots of rubbish food and Disney films, curled up on the sofa, under the blankets. Paris loves it. It's all she ever wants – attention and time. I love it too, but right now I need to get back to work. My demons have been put to rest and I'm back at the computer, logging on to see if my target has replied.

He has. 'I'm going to be really rude, but I don't think I do. Try jogging my memory? x'

A kiss. Well, if Ben or anyone I was dating was putting kisses on the end of his messages to random women, I wouldn't be happy!

'Aw this upsets me. :-(… I came and worked at your call centre a couple of weeks ago, as a temp. In the admin department. You brought me enough paperwork!' I reply. Jenny had told me he works in a call centre, and has confirmed that they take on temporary staff. It's a plausible story. When you work in a call centre with over 200 people, and have temps coming in and out every day, people don't always remember everyone. What is rather surprising, though, is how quickly a reply comes through.

'Ahhh, I thought you looked familiar. That must be where I know you from! You wore glasses at work right? How you doing? Sorry for all the paperwork. xx'

TWO kisses. Flipping heck! Pushing the boat out now. A friend of mine once advised me on what is acceptable as far as kisses are concerned. I only ever used to put one kiss on my texts, and she had a fit. That was apparently pathetic. The rule is one kiss for friends and family and two kisses for boyfriends all the time. No exception. She only ever put one kiss to her boyfriend when she was pissed off at him. Three kisses was meant for special occasions and any more meant you wanted sex. I asked a couple of the girls about this because I thought she was talking nonsense. Turns out other people believe the same thing. So what does it mean when someone entirely random, someone you don't know, who is certainly not a boyfriend, puts on two kisses? Maybe I should text my friend and ask her? I don't have time though …

'I'm great thanks. Glad you've finally placed my face! You were making me feel a little sad then! Not sure if

I'll be coming back to work with you lot any time soon :-(xx'

I go with two kisses as well. You never know where it may lead.

'Now that is a sad situation! Can you not come back just to do my paperwork and sod everyone else? xxx'

Oh my God ... THREE kisses! He's clearly online, so I'm going to strike while the iron is hot on this situation. I turn on the chat facility. Usually I keep it off or we generally get random people pinging up, asking who we are and how we know them. Clearly they're puzzled because we actually don't know any of them! It gets far too annoying, so we keep it off. This, however, is a special occasion.

'Hiya! Thought I'd save the mails ;-)' I message him. And I'm right, he's there and typing. I feel nervous. Bit strange this, chatting to someone you actually don't know as someone you're not. More than a bit strange, actually. Really damn strange.

'Hiya!!!!!!! I agree, this is much simpler!'

OK, not much to go on there. Hmm ... 'So tell me more about you! I'm a bit too shy in real life to actually drum up the courage to speak to cute people ;-)' Ramping it up a notch.

'Cute eh? I like that! You're not too bad yourself! Well, I'm just me. Average guy. LOVE motorbikes, my total passion. Hate work, don't we all! How about you? I know absolutely nothing! xxx'

'Yes cute! ;-) Me ... Half my family have motorbikes, bit scary if you ask me! I love work, most days. Depends where I end up though. I'd hate being in the same place all the time! Sad I've left your place though. Was lots of eye candy! xxx'

'Oh really. Don't tell me. You liked Jason in accounts?! Everyone does. Hate the guy myself, but he seems to do something for the ladies! With the motorbike thing, I reckon you've just not had a good enough driver ;-) xxx'

'Ha, ha. No. Jason didn't do it for me, I'm afraid. I was actually just meaning you, and one other. Not that I'm telling you who that was! Hmm, your motorbike idea sounds more like an offer to me! Had a few drivers but none have converted me! xxx'

'It was an offer, if you're ever up for it! I think you're too chicken though personally. Surprised at the Jason thing. Although I never got what it was that the women fall for! What kind of motorbikes have you been on? xxx'

Oh gosh, time for a Google search: 'cool motorbikes'. Some green effort pops onto the screen that looks cool – I'll go with that one. 'My brother had a kawasaggi or whatever they're called. It was bright green and very fast! Bit scared of your offer. How do I know you're a safe driver? xxx'

'Ladies are ALWAYS in safe hands with me! Do you mean a Kawasaki? Bit of a poser's bike that one. xxx'

'LadieS, huh? How many ladies have you been taking on your bike!? xxx'

'Oh, you know, one or two! Good boy me! Can't you see the halo around my head? xxx'

'Funny that, one thing I didn't notice about you, haha. xxx'

'That's interesting. What exactly did you notice then? You mustn't have been looking hard enough! xxxx'

FOUR? No, that's a boat too far for me!

'What do you think I was looking at? lol xxx' Back to three!

'My big knob?????? xxx'

OH MY GOD! 'LOL' And I really, truly am laughing out loud! Mainly with embarrassment, even though I'm on my own. I look around me, just to check. Yep, still just me. I'm sure I've gone bright red. I wonder at what point we decide that the job is done and the game is over? I'm going to have to develop an alter ego for this kind of thing. Normal Rebecca would probably shut down the computer right now and die of shame for the next thirty minutes. Detective Rebecca needs to get a grip and reply with something flirtatious – and quick!

'Well, personally I didn't manage to see that, being the good girl that I am and all that. xxx' That was a bit lame!

'Good girl!? Really? Are you sure about that? xxx'

'Of course I'm sure! I'm a total angel! When do I get to play on the bike then? xxx'

'All in good time, beautiful! So, where exactly do you live? xxx'

'Not too far, about five miles from you I believe. xxx' Ooops! Jenny had told me where he lived. I hoped he wouldn't be suspicious that I knew, but he must have supposed I'd found out from someone at the call centre. He must assume I'd been asking questions about him!

'Oh really? I hate this place! It's vile. xxx'

'Why do you say that? xxx'

'Too many pathetic little kids that think they're hard and want to fight me! xxx'

'Really!? You didn't strike me as the type. xxx'

'I'm not, and that's the problem. I used to be a fighter in the old days, but now I'm just a chilled out laid-back kinda guy who wants an easy life. Far too many people around here won't let me do that. Stresses me out. Just want to move and get away! xxx' He's opening up.

'Sounds like there's quite a lot of depth to you. If it's so bad, why don't you move? I LOVE bad boys though. Really can't resist them, but totally know that I should! xxx'

'I will eventually, just difficult at the moment. I certainly tick the bad boy category for you! What's your relationship status anyway? xxx'

'I had a fiancé, but we split up a month or so ago. He was a real bad boy, in every sense of the word. We have a little girl together. He's pretty good with her, takes her out every weekend. Loving being single at the moment to be honest, a lot less hassle. Obviously though there are some drawbacks. xxx'

'I know exactly what you mean there. What split you up? xxx'

'He cheated on me. How's your relationship doing? xxx' Now for the crunch.

'As if!!!!!! Someone so hot, and he cheated on you!? Must have been mad! Mine, it's OK. Nothing to write home about, I guess. Hardly ground-breaking, or earth-moving, if you know what I mean? xxx'

I'm finding this a bit disturbing. I am a total stranger to this guy. The pictures of me are fakes, the profile is fake and all of the information I'm telling him is fake – and yet he's opening up his life in an evening. Scary, really scary! Oh well, I'll keep going. This is exactly what we're supposed to be finding out.

'Think I know what you mean, but feel free to spell it out for me :-D Yes, he cheated … a lot. Probably a blessing in disguise if you ask me. xxx'

He went back to talking about his girlfriend. 'It's just boring. We're more friends than anything else. Can't see it lasting forever if I'm really honest. Always looking for something to spice up my life ;-) xxxx'

Oh, how I feel sorry for our poor client Jenny.

'How do you mean, spice up your life? ;-) xxx' He doesn't half dance around what he wants to say!

'You know, bit of fun, bit of excitement. Sexy girls like you! xxx'

Is this it? Can I conclude the case now? No, I suppose I had better see whether he would go all the way, so to speak.

'What about girls like me? Come on, let's spit it out!!!! xxx'

'OK,' comes the reply. 'I'll spit it out. I want to f★★k your brains out. xxxx'

I nearly fall backwards off my chair! My eyes are wide open, and I'm stunned. My hand is placed firmly over my wide-open mouth, and if I wasn't highly embarrassed before, I sure am now! Come on, Rebecca, grow some nuts and reply!

'That's nice to know! When would you like to do that then??? xxx' That's nice to know? *Nice to know!?* I sound like a right prude! Nice ... nice ... I huff and puff to myself for ten minutes. I spin around and around in my chair, and then it dawns on me. Oh my goodness, he's not replying! A very slow panic begins to build inside my stomach. Did I blow it? What if I blew it? Oh, for goodness' sake.

Thirty minutes pass. Nothing. Go downstairs, make coffee. Go back to the computer – nothing. Reply to some emails, speak to mother, do an online shop. Look back at Facebook – nothing. He could just be busy. Go and put Paris to bed. Read Paris her bedtime story, I have no idea what it was. Words came out of my mouth, but again nothing went into my brain. We have goodnight kisses then I slip into the office and sneakily look at the computer through one eye, as if to prolong the suspense. Nothing. Slam the laptop shut! I have a little debate with myself for the next thirty minutes about whether I should tell the client yet, and decide against it for now. I'll leave it till morning, and if I've heard nothing I'll contact her then. I never send results to people late at night, because if they pick up the email they might not sleep. Results are always received better in the morning.

The rest of the evening goes as slowly as it possibly can. I try to eat my dinner, but I feel a bit sick at what I've done. Would that guy have flirted if I hadn't started it first? Yes, I'm sure he would have. There's no question. But does it mean he would actually be unfaithful? Is it enough to end a relationship? I attempt to watch soaps, but realise I'm not registering anything. What's wrong with me? This kind of suspense is more stressful than a surveillance job. I wonder if it was because I was almost there, but at the moment of victory it was snatched away. The emotional turmoil and guilt that I felt in the beginning has slowly subsided and the business person in me has once again resurfaced. I realise I truly want to get my job done, and get the result. What he's said is quite damning. I'd hate any partner of mine to send this kind of content to another person, real or not real. I couldn't bear it if Ben did anything like this. My thoughts go back to Jenny, my client, and the little girl who looks so much like Paris. Yep, time to get a grip again!

That night I go to bed, and finally make my last check of the computer at 2.14am – nothing.

The following morning, my mother collects Paris and takes her to playschool so I can get some sleep. Apparently she thinks I look 'ropey'. Fabulous. My dream is full of spiders and snakes, the dream I usually have when I'm stressed. Sometimes when I'm exceptionally stressed I literally see them in my sleep and jump out of bed screaming, but thankfully I'm not at that dire stress level just yet.

First thing I do when I get up is walk down the hallway to the office and start up the computer. I sit staring in a daze at the screen and sign in to Facebook. I don't even wait for the usual flatulence email noises to stop, which upsets the computer and makes it run slow. I'll never learn, and I'll never have patience.

Facebook loads – nothing. I literally stand up in my nightie and stomp my feet. Now I'm mad. Coffee is called for before I ring the client and let her know what he said yesterday.

I make coffee, and take it back upstairs, then pick up the phone and dial our client.

'Well, I don't have conclusive evidence for you, but I do have some quite disturbing correspondence,' I tell her, trying my best to hide my stressed-out tone.

'Really?' she says, and she doesn't sound sad, happy or relieved. Odd.

'Really. It's not good, and I wouldn't be happy but he's said he would like to "sleep" with me in rather graphic language.'

'Oh, as if!' She sounds miffed now.

'I know. I'm sending you the transcript as we speak.'

'Thanks. How's it been left with him?' Just the question I didn't want.

'To be honest, he said what he wanted to do to me, and I asked him when. Now he's not replied since yesterday.'

'Interesting. What time was this?' She's still pretty chilled.

I tell her.

'He was supposed to be at work then! That's strange. Has he said much else?'

'Not much else, but he did say that you two are more friends now.'

'What is he like!'

'I have to say, you seem remarkably calm.'

'Do you know what? I really don't care what he's got to say. I just want out. I'm not surprised, but I don't feel angry or sad or anything. Is that strange?'

Aw, she's so lovely. Very level-headed, which I love! Makes my life a lot easier.

'There's nothing strange about how you feel. No one writes a rulebook on this kind of thing. If you're angry, that's normal; if you're sad, it's normal; and if you don't care … well, that's normal too!' I was talking from my own experience because I'd been through all those emotions when James cheated on me – and then some.

She laughs. 'I think you're right.'

'In a couple of days you may feel entirely different, but right now anything goes.' I try to reassure her, and it's all the truth. There's no such thing as 'normal' when it comes to the way human beings react to emotional upsets.

'Thanks so much. It's really helpful talking to you. I'll go and read what he's written and get back to you. What's going to happen now?'

'I'll wait and see if he replies, and if he hasn't in the next couple of days I'll send something back. Unless you read what he's put and decide it's enough?'

I say my goodbyes and hang up the phone.

A couple of hours pass and I go from checking the computer once every thirty seconds, to once every thirty minutes. Finally at 8pm that evening he replies to my question about when we're going to meet.

'All in good time my dear, all in good time! xxx'

As if! He has kept me waiting all this time, ready for the end of the journey and 'all in good time' is the most he can say. What a spoon!

'Oh no you don't. You can't say something like that and then let me down with a rubbish response. "All in good time" isn't quite cutting it for me. xxx' That is probably the most truthful thing I've said in this whole online conversation.

'Lol. Don't all good things come to those who wait? xxx'

He's online. Brilliant! Let's bring him down and end this now. 'Maybe they do. I, on the other hand, have no patience, and want all my good things right now! xxx'

'Oh, bossy one, are we?! Are you as bossy in bed as you are on chat? xxx'

'I'd like to think so, but well done at dodging my question!!!! :-(xxx'

'Not dodging the question. I know exactly what's going to happen. I just like to tease you a bit more. Does it turn you on?? xxx'

Oh dear, here he goes again. This is where all my big talk fails! The alter ego needs to come back right now. Fortunately she shows up right on time. 'Of course it does. I'm not good with people who are all talk. I like them to put their money where their mouth is! xxx'

'Where else do you want my mouth? xxx'

Shit!!!! … What the hell do I say now? I've gone all flustered, because this is way too creepy for me. I'm grimacing and wafting my face with my hands to cool it down while trying not to touch the keyboard in case it will bite me, or something equally as stupid.

'Where do you want to put it!? xxx' Question dodged! Relief. I'm now tensed for his reply.

'Everywhere I shouldn't do! xxx'

'Why shouldn't you? xxx'

'My other half won't be very pleased with me, but I can't help it. I want you so bad! xxx'

I need him to arrange a date so this can be all over. 'Really? Well, no, I guess she wouldn't be too pleased about you wanting to jump into bed with someone else. Have you done it before? xxx' Talk about cutting to the chase.

'Only a couple of times, mainly accidents on nights out. But I want to take my time with you. xxx'

Bingo! That's a tick in a box somewhere – admitting he's cheated. Thank you, I'll take that!

'Oh really? In what way? You mean you're going to make me wait? xxx'

'You said you wanted a bad boy. I'll be your bad boy in every way you possibly want! And no, I'm not going to make you wait for it. I meant I'm going to take my time over sexing you up! That OK? xxx'

'Blimey. I can't wait. I just need to know when and where this is going to happen. Too excited to wait any longer.' Come on! Name me a day, and a place! I'm literally bouncing in my chair, clapping my hands together, ready for the consolation.

'You mean you're really going to give me your punani? xxx'

I stare at the screen, very confused. 'Punani'? What the hell's that? I'm too confused to be mad that he dodged the question again. Bloody player, does he not realise he's messing me around? Fool. After a few more seconds the clouds lift, and I understand. Punani, another name for female lady bits!

I burst out laughing. What a total tool! Who the hell calls it a 'punani'?

'Of course. You've turned me on so much, I can't wait any longer. You're driving me totally mad with all your question dodging. Tell me when! xxx' I sit and shake my head in silence. The fool.

'Tomorrow?'

That's all I need. I jump up and do the fancy dance – a shuffle of my feet crossed with the MC Hammer dance – that's fast becoming my signature when I get a result.

'I'm there! When and where? xxx'

'Say 3.30pm at the Levens Hotel in town? xxx'

That's what you call a conclusion! 'Absolutely, I'm so looking forward to it. xxx'

'Me too! Do you want me to bring any toys? xxx'

Whhhhhat? This guy's lost the plot, I think. What a strange question! 'I'll bring my own ;-) xxx Going to have to go though, got to work. My Facebook is linked to my phone, so if you need me just message. Don't want to get your number, just in case with girlfriend and all that … xxx'

'Good idea. I'm looking forward to it too. I'll see you then. xxx'

I copy the whole transcript and email it straight to our client. I text her to say we've got a conclusion, and that if she wants to contact me for a chat she can. An hour later, she does just that. Her number flashes up on the phone and I answer, not knowing how she's going to react.

'How funny was that?' she exclaims.

Well, that's unexpected! 'You mean the punani thing?' I was expecting a screaming or sobbing woman at the end of the phone and don't quite know how to react.

'Yeah. How stupid is he?'

'Oh, I know. Made me think the same thing!' I wonder if she's putting a brave face on it, or if she actually doesn't care.

'I don't know how to react. I've read it all three times over and I've got no feelings about it. I just want to get out.'

I feel sorry that she's had to resort to this and am trying to think how to respond when she surprises me again.

'I know this is going to sound really strange, but can you continue corresponding with him?' There's a pause and I don't have a clue what to say. 'It's just that while he's been chatting to you online he's been really happy and chirpy around us. He's like a whole other person. It's as if you've brightened him up and distracted him.'

I'm slowly beginning to understand.

'Really. So do you mean you want us to keep up the inter-action?' I ask, being very cautious, just in case I've totally misunderstood this situation.

'That's exactly it. I want you to keep him distracted while I move out. If he's talking to you and happy, he won't realise what I'm doing. My friend and I are getting a house together, but it's going to take two weeks to go through. I don't want this blowing up just yet.'

How very odd. It's beginning to sound like one of our crazier cases, but on some weird level I get her. I understand exactly what she's talking about. For the next two weeks, Steph, Jess, Helen and I keep up the story. We make excuses about why we can't meet him, as he gets more and more impatient, and more graphic. It's a good job Jenny's house move goes through when it does, because I don't know how much longer we could have kept up the correspondence.

In the end she does confront him, and she does leave. He cries for weeks, apparently, but she is truly happy living with her daughter. It gets crazy again though. I catch up with Jenny again over a year and a half later and she tells me they split for over six months, and then got back together. Now she tells me that their relationship is the best it's ever been and they want to get married. She still believes she needed to hire us to honey trap him. It gave him the wake-up call he needed, apparently. He certainly won't try any more online flirting in future.

I really like Jenny. She's a lovely lady. I don't know if it's because our daughters look so alike, or that we are a similar age, but her case really disturbed me. I honestly feel some kind of connection to her. It broke all my boundaries, my morals, distressed me and finally made me understand, but one way or the other … I truly get her! I wouldn't necessarily recommend this strategy to anyone else, unless they had genuinely thought through the repercussions and weighed up all they had to lose. But in Jenny's case, it did the trick in the end.

HONEY TRAP,
HONEY TRAP

I'm having a crisis! Not a mid-life version, and not a mental breakdown version. I don't even know what kind of crisis this is, but I know I'm having one. I think I love my job, but I have doubts. Am I doing the right thing? Is it right to interfere in other people's relationships the way we're doing? Could we sometimes do more harm than good? And if things work out between me and Ben, surely at some point he's going to start complaining about the anti-social hours and the fact that I can never plan far in advance in case I suddenly have to shoot off and follow someone on the other side of the country?

Would he complain if he knew about the online flirting I did with Jenny's fiancé? Or would he understand it's just part of the job? We don't discuss my work at all but I can't imagine him being unreasonable about it if he knew.

Today I sit here writing to you from the middle of absolutely nowhere. I couldn't even tell you where I am, geographically, except that it's somewhere in the Lake District. Yesterday I decided enough was enough, that Ben and I needed to spend some quality time together and I needed space to think about my life, so I dived online. I looked at places to go that weren't too far or too close either, and here we are in the Lakes. He's currently inside playing a game of pool all by himself. Bless.

We're staying in a beautiful Georgian manor house that's been split into several apartments. Not that you ever see anyone else; I feel very much as if I'm lady of my own manor right now. Our apartment is stunning: all oak panelling, with a very 'murder mystery' feel. That's ironic, I guess. I never accounted for that in my whole 'run away from my job and think' plan. One fake oak wall opens up into our bedroom, and the other into the kitchen. We've spent the past twenty-four hours doing very little. Scrabble has been played a ridiculous number of times. Don't tell Ben, but I've cheated at every game. When he isn't looking, I switch my letter tiles. I would go on the Internet application that gives you words for the letters you've got, but there's no Internet reception in this middle-of-nowhere Georgian mansion. Darn it. Still, I've won nine games, he's won two, and he can't quite figure out where my new-found brilliance has come from. Personally I think it's his own fault for not paying enough attention.

We've strolled into the village twice: once for morning bacon, the other to have hot chocolate at the local chocolate factory. I kid you not. The only two shops this village has are a corner shop and a chocolate factory. Random.

While Ben is indoors playing pool, I'm sitting on the front doorstep. Although it's a bit too grand to be called a 'doorstep' – more like 'extravagant entrance at the end of a gravel drive-way'. It's a beautifully sunny day, and warm. Bunnies are hopping around on the lawn, and I'm finally getting to do what I wanted to do. Reflect.

I can't put my finger on the problem. Has this job totally distorted my views on life? Have I finally cracked under the strain of all the horror stories? It's highly possible. When we started this journey of opening the agency, my mission was clear. My goals were to create an understanding and affordable service for people who had nowhere else to turn. I truly believe there is a need for it. I spout my views so much, I'm not even sure if I believe them any more. I don't know if I'm just saying that because I'm a defensive person and, as my daddy always tells me, 'I'm never wrong'. I know I will literally argue the toss with anyone, about anything, until the cows come home. When people ask me if I have an opinion on something, I always do. I'm so darn opinionated I frustrate myself. My brain literally feels mashed into a cloud of opinions. I don't actually know what's real and what's not any more.

What if all the critics are right? Some people claim this industry is all about making money from heartbreak, and preying on the weak. What if they are right? How do I know they're not? What if this whole time I've been totally delusional? Maybe this is why I need to run away from the world, and hide myself in the middle of nowhere. I need to find out if I'm delusional.

Ben on the other hand seems fine with it all. He doesn't really have an opinion on what I do. He never probes me, or questions anything. Perhaps he's worried there might be a conflict of interest if I tell him too much about what I get up to, him being in the police force. If I say I'm working, he just says 'OK'. That's it. It's not that he doesn't care about what I do, I know that. It's usually the people who have something to hide who have issues with it. He doesn't, so to me it's only a good sign.

People ring and ask us for help. We tell them how we can help, and try to offer advice as best we can. Now I know for certain I always make myself clear. I'm no counsellor but I talk from personal experience. What if that's wrong? What if all the other detectives who are cold and distant, keeping to the facts, are right? What if I'm taking these people's lives and putting words and thoughts into their heads. Oh my goodness.

I start to think back to the people we've helped. They tell me our service has been useful because we gave them somewhere to turn when they had nowhere else. I know when I was dealing with an unfaithful partner I would have been truly grateful for someone on the end of the phone who cared about what I was saying – and I do care. Really I do. When they tell me their stories, it bothers me. After a while I even feel I know them, although in reality I don't. I think there's something quite sad in that.

I'm not a person to sit around and dwell on drama, so why am I doing it now? The way I see it, I have two options. One, I carry on regardless. I keep doing what I'm doing and put my own personal views to the back of my brain. A little bit like I've been doing since the agency started. The doubts will recur from time to time, but if they do I'll just keep running away to Georgian mansions with chocolate factories on the doorstep. Chocolate solves everything, right?

Or then there's option two. The option I don't like to think about: I close up shop. Change our phone numbers, take the website down and go live a normal life. It sounds so simple, but instinctively I know that's not what I want. Yes, I doubt myself – but I hate the thought of giving up what I've built even more. No, I'll stand my ground, I'll remember my dad saying that 'I'm never wrong' … Then I'll hope and pray that I'm right!

For the first time in a while I feel the fog in my brain is lifting. I look up at the sky, and the beautiful blue creeping through makes the moment feel semi-magical. What am I saying? I'm not usually this much of a floaty airy-fairy type! For goodness' sake, I'm going soft. I'm shaking my head as I look down at my phone, lying on the step next to me. It's on silent, but it's flashing. Someone is calling. Bearing in mind I'm literally in the middle of nowhere and I only get phone reception on these steps, I could take the call and risk it unprofessionally cutting out mid-conversation, or I could just leave it. I'm supposed to be having a break, and the wonderful Ben is waiting indoors for me. I should ignore it. So why do I see my hand reaching towards it?

'Hello,' I answer. Oops!

'Hi, is this The Lady Detective Agency?' It's a man's voice, with a distinctly Glaswegian accent but fortunately one that I seem to be able to make out.

'It is,' I tell him. I'm feeling upbeat. Clarifying the nonsense in my head has made me feel refreshed.

'Excellent. I wanted to talk to you about honey trapping.'

Instantly I feel dread in the pit of my stomach. Honey trapping scares me. Of course, I've done the online version now, and that caused me all kinds of moral dilemmas, but the face-to-face kind is different again. My head sinks into my hands, with the phone still glued to my ear.

'OK,' I say, wishing I had actually just left the phone alone.

'It's my sister's boyfriend I need honey trapping.'

'Oh, your sister's boyfriend?' I try to make the surprise in my voice not too obvious.

'Yes, that's right. He's such a moron. I can't stand him and I know he's up to no good. He's a really smooth big shot who gives the time of day to any dodgy-looking woman who will talk to him. I've been on nights out with him and he makes me feel sick.'

'Really, OK, um, well … Does your sister know you want to take this course of action?'

'No, no, I could never tell her. I want to surprise her with the evidence. I'll never tell her how I got it. I just want her to think he did something on a night out and I've got the pictures to prove it. I don't want her to know I hired a private investigator, or set him up. Is that OK?'

'Well, it's not something we've done before, but nothing surprises me any more – so it's fine with me.'

'Excellent. I want pictures that will make her dump him, no questions asked. Even if he doesn't fall for anything, I want your girls literally throwing themselves at him. I just need him gone from our family's life.'

I feel very uneasy about this and am tempted to turn the job down and tell him where to go. 'We can't literally throw ourselves at him. We'll be overly flirtatious, but we can't just kiss him if he doesn't indicate he's willing. It's too far out of the box for us, I'm afraid.' I try to plead my case as politely as I possibly can. This client is really persistent, though, and he seems like a cheeky chappy. The type you struggle to say no to. The actual words of the conversation are rather disturbing, but the manner in which they're spoken make it light-hearted. You know underneath he's deadly serious though. Yes, I'm disturbed.

'If he wants to go to bed with anyone, can you accommodate that too?' he asks.

Why on earth am I still having this conversation? I'm not sure whether his tone is joking or serious but I fear it's the latter. I laugh it off and tell him a kiss is as far as we will go and that's just that, then I try to get him off the phone as quickly as I can.

I know I've said we'll do it, but I really don't think we should. I ring Steph straight away and tell her what's been said. She's equally disturbed but says something along the lines that it's not our place to question it. If this is what the client wants, we should give it to him. We can't pick and choose the jobs we take because of our morals or we'd never take on any job. There's always an element somewhere that we question and don't like.

In the end I get over myself and arrange the details and logistics. He wants us to go up to Glasgow. Steph and I decide to hire a honey trap expert based up there specially for the evening so we don't have to do it ourselves and can learn from her. We're too new at this and the job could potentially be difficult. I'd never do it myself even if I was single, and certainly not now that I'm gradually building a relationship with the lovely Ben. It's just not in me. Even when I *was* single I couldn't simply approach men and flirt, so to do it professionally would be torture. I'm already off to hell for my past misdemeanours, so I don't need to add any more to my rap sheet!

I pick up Steph and we drive to collect Jess, who is getting off a flight from Benidorm. I asked Helen first, but she has to babysit for her niece. Sat in the airport waiting area we mull over the details.

'I don't really feel right about this,' Steph says in her gloomy voice.

'Me neither. You know when you get that Monday morning feeling on a Sunday night, like you are totally dreading going to work?'

'Yep.'

'Well, I feel like that! I can't get excited, I just want it over and done with.'

'I know what you mean. It's just strange. We're not going to test if he will be unfaithful, or even find out if he's done anything previously. We're going to try and *make* him cheat. It's just strange.'

I don't think there's ever been a job we've questioned as much as we're doing right now. Jess appears through the doors with her suitcases, sombrero and everything.

'Hiya!' she shouts in a super-cheery tone with a big wave. We both wave back miserably. 'What the heck is wrong with you two?' She's super-tanned, even though she's only been away for a week.

'We're not comfortable,' Steph says.

'Good holiday?' I ask.

'Fabulous. If you're not comfortable sit on the other seats, you idiots.' She looks confused.

'Not the seats, you doughnut – the job we're about to do. We're not comfortable with it.' Steph puts on her sombrero and tells her about it as we walk towards the car park.

'OOOOOOh!' The penny finally drops for Jess. 'Well, what's the real issue?'

'Just that we're literally setting up a man to fail. It's like we're trapping him. We've always argued the toss against critics of honey trapping, saying it can be useful. But I don't see how this can possibly be useful.'

'I see where you're coming from, but you're committed now, aren't you? We can't tell him we're not doing it.'

'No, that would be unprofessional. We're just going to have to see what happens and use it as a learning experience,' I tell her.

★   ★   ★

Next up, we're off to Glasgow with me behind the wheel. We've been given the names of bars the target usually attends, so on the way there Steph is checking them out on Google Earth.

'It looks pretty easy to me. He mainly stays in the same part of town and just goes in one pub after the other. There's a start point and end point. He shouldn't be too difficult to find.' She looks pleased with herself. Jess is snoring away in the back seat of the car with the sombrero over her face. 'I'm going to pinch that from her later,' Steph tells me, glancing over. We seem to be getting over the fit of conscience and becoming our old selves again, a fact that is confirmed to me when Jess wakes an hour later, and they're both singing at the top of their lungs to Bon Jovi.

We approach Glasgow over half an hour late, thanks to having to wait for Jess's plane. Both Steph and Jess get changed into their outfits in the car. Steph dons a pair of very tight black satin trousers and a sheer black T-shirt, while Jess is in an ultra-mini skirt and vest top. They both do their make-up in the car, and I have great fun taking corners as fast as I can while they're applying their mascara! I pull up just down the road from the bar where we're meeting the honey trapper and I do my own quick change. I go a little conservative with a tight black pencil skirt and sparkly gold top. Doing this job you become an expert at changing clothes literally anywhere!

We walk into the bar where honey trap lady is supposed to be. I've phoned the people she gave as references and by all accounts she seems good at what she does. And from the conversations we've had over the phone, she sounds bubbly and happy, very similar to us.

We spot her within seconds, but I realise straight away that she looks a lot more glam in her pictures than in person. An alarm bell rings in my head.

'Amy?' I ask her, and she stands up and gives me a hug.

'Hiiiiiiii, loves.'

'Hi, nice to finally meet you.'

Steph and Jess introduce themselves and I weigh her up. Her profile said she was early thirties, but she's almost forty I'm sure. Her hair is dyed white platinum blonde and short. Her skin is seriously fake-tanned, and that's coming from me! I'm used to seeing the residents of Manchester douse themselves in forty layers, topped up by sunbeds, but this is potentially on an Oompa Loompa scale of tan. Other than that, the rest of her passes.

'So how long have you been doing this?' Jess asks.

'About five years. I'm one of the originals, lovey. Lots of people are going into the industry now, but I was doin' this when no one had ever heard of it.'

'Will you take on any job at all?' I ask her, genuinely interested.

'Course I would. I don't care who or what it is. I just like the money. It does pay well.'

I smile back at her, but it's quickly becoming clear that her rules of the trade are very different from the ones we try to work by.

Steph gives me a glance as if to say 'Where on earth did you find this woman?'

Jess starts to brief her. 'Here's all the documents: the emails from the client and pictures of the target. How well do you know Glasgow?'

'Ach, very well, love. It's ma home town. Rebecca sent over some of these emails earlier in the week. This client of yours sure wants the guy nailing right!' She's so enthusiastic about the job, it's alarming!

'Yes, you could say that.' I'm slowly beginning to think I've misjudged her. Her personality is fine, but her morals and passion to screw people over are a worry. I'm still finding it ironic that just over a week ago, I was sat on those mansion steps contemplating my own morals. Now I've been thrust into something I'm totally uncomfortable with. It's as if someone is looking over me and dishing me up the worst-case scenario that I could ever be thrown into. I suppose there's one point to be made: if I survive tonight, I'll be able to survive anything.

'So what exactly are you going to do? How do you play out this kind of thing?' Steph asks.

'What? You loveys have never done this?'

Jess shakes her head and, as Amy looks over her shoulder to check no one's listening, Steph whispers in my ear, 'If she calls me love or lovey just one more time …'

'I'll tell ya how I do it. I flirt, lovey.' Steph is clenching her teeth, eyes wide open. It's the first time I've smiled since we got here. 'Then I flirt some more, and keep on goin' until they cave.'

I wonder how I say to her that I don't like this idea? 'What made you get into it?' I ask her.

'Ma ex-boyfriend was an arsehole,' she replies in her fine Glaswegian accent. 'He cheated on me all the time. Left, right, centre. You name it, he did it. I needed some kind of proof, though – ya know? So I got one of ma friends to lure him ta her apartment one night and boom! He took the bait. It made me start thinkin' that I could do it as a job. Ya know – catch the cheatin' bastards.'

Oh my lord. This woman is everything we're not. Don't get me wrong – she's lovely and friendly, but wow! Totally not what we do or who we are. We're not bitter and we don't have a vendetta against all men. We understand that people are unfaithful, and simply go out to find the truth. This woman seems like she has a score to settle with the world.

Jess has been to the bar and got us a round of soft drinks. Only problem is her drink doesn't look very soft. It's a milky yellow colour with a mini umbrella and a cherry on top. I raise an eyebrow in her direction as she slurps it through a straw. She retaliates with an equally high eyebrow and a 'Whhhhhat? It's just one,' in her best whining voice.

I roll my eyes to the ceiling and return my attention to Amy.

'My ex-husband wasn't very faithful either,' I tell her. 'I tried to hire private investigators but they were really cold and unsympathetic. We opened up the agency so people have somewhere to turn where we care what happens to them, and that's why they contact us. Honey trapping is just one service we offer, but we're really not comfortable with it. I'm only being honest. You love it and have so much passion, and you're so friendly. I just don't want you to think we're not enthusiastic or anything.'

'Ach no, I get it, my love.' Steph kicks me under the table. It hurts. 'It's not for everyone, so it's a good job ya called me. I'll help ya out.'

'Shall we go now?' Steph asks.

'Good plan. You ready, Amy?'

'Aye, love.' Steph kicks me again. It hurts again. Jess begins to down her drink really fast.

'If you end up on the floor …' I start.

'I'm not having any more. Promise. Just need one for courage.'

As we're walking out of the bar and on to the next one, Steph and I hang back while Jess chats to Amy.

'Proper hardcore honey trapper, this woman,' she comments.

'I know she is. It's so not right, is it? It's like she's going after her prey at any cost. We need a massive debrief after this job to figure out why we have so many issues with it. I'm actually debating not offering it any more. It's just wrong to me.'

Steph agrees. 'I'm so far out of my comfort zone that I'm on the edge of outer space. I tell you now, though, every time she says "love" or "lovey" I'm going to kick you for fun!'

I smile sweetly at her. 'Lovely, that's just what I need.'

Between us we figure out our cover story. We're long-lost friends from university. We all went to uni in Manchester to study fashion. We still live pretty local to there, but Amy is from Glasgow. We've travelled up for the weekend to explore the city and see our old pal.

'Sometimes I tell people I'm an actress and not a honey trapper. It's a total act the whole time, and I get paid for it, so it all makes sense ta me.'

To be fair, it's one of the most sensible things Amy has said all evening.

We head into the first bar, which is utterly packed with people. I must have looked at the pictures of the target twenty times but how on earth we're going to spot him in here, I don't know. It's a total needle in a haystack job.

At the next bar we split into twos and take separate ends. It's busy, but not like the last place.

We're two hours into the time he's expected to have been out drinking. By now, he should be in full swing. We also have pictures of his friends, but we spot absolutely no one.

Five bars and a lot of soft drinks later and we're starting to get doubtful. We've all gone really quiet and are hardly speaking to each other. That's when you know there's a problem. When the shit is hitting the fan, we go quiet. Maybe the Almighty is looking down on us and dishing out only bad stuff this week.

Just as I'm losing the will to carry on, thinking that fate has stepped in to make us leave our prey alone, Amy taps my arm. She points at the corner of the bar with a huge smile on her face.

I message Jess and Steph to join us at the corner, and we all arrive at the same time. It's a roped-off VIP section. I spot our prey immediately, along with three of the friends we've been sent pictures of. They're all surrounded by women. It's as if they're footballers and have young girls literally falling at their feet. In reality, I know he's not a footballer; he's a computer programmer with a taste for luxury – or so our client has told me.

'Hmm … How do we get behind that little rope effort?' Steph asks.

'I have no idea. Why don't we sit down at that table?' I suggest, pointing at one that's free and overlooks the VIP section. 'Then we wait for them to move. We've got all night. If we don't get them here we can get them at the next bar, or even the next one. If he does something with one of these women between now and then, it's better than us throwing ourselves at him. At least that way it will be natural. We just need evidence of it.'

We all agree that's the best course of action, and for the next fifteen minutes my conscience is clear.

'He *is* rather dashing,' Amy muses.

'I can't bloody see!' Steph chirps up. 'I've forgotten my glasses, and they're too far away.' Both Steph and I are blind as bats when it comes to distance viewing, so I'm struggling too. I'm pulling a face that the girls always tell me off for, in which I squint my eyes, raise my head slightly and my top lip goes up so I look like a horse. They all hate it and tell me it's my 'ugly face'.

'What are ya doin'?' Amy asks me.

'Sorry,' I say, regaining normal composure. 'It helps me to see a little better'.

'I say he's dashing alright!' Jess throws her views into the conversation. I get out my phone again and look at his pictures, which Steph is leaning over my shoulder to peek at too.

'Yeah, I suppose he is rather OK,' she agrees.

'Would you want to honey trap him?' I ask, raising an eyebrow.

'Um. I might.'

'Ooooo …' says Jess.

'Yeah, if I stay single I don't mind striking up a conversation or two with the good-looking variety,' Steph says to me with a hint of sarcasm, and I know exactly why.

A few months ago we had another honey trap job come in. I believed Steph – who's been single for a while, and is a very stunning lady – was the right candidate for the job. Only when I showed her the picture she didn't really think so. The target was about sixteen stone – and I don't mean sixteen stone of muscle. He was five foot ten, in his fifties. He had dyed blond hair with black roots, and what's more he only had one leg! I turned the job down on the basis that if Steph had honey trapped him, it would have been entrapment. He would never have believed a slim, petite, stunning blonde lady would be interested in him. Steph was not impressed I even suggested the idea, and would never have accepted the job in a million years. That's why right now she's having her little dig.

'These women are literally falling all over him,' Jess says in amazement.

'If he's not a cheater, loveys,' – I brace myself for Steph's kick, but it doesn't come – 'then I don't know who is,' says Amy.

Kick. I relaxed too soon.

'Hopefully he'll do something with one of these little lot and we can clear off back home,' I say.

'Are ya stayin' the night?' Amy asks.

'We've got accommodation booked. Right now I just want to have a cup of tea and go to bed,' I tell her.

'Me too,' agrees Steph.

'Are you the party animal then?' she asks Jess.

'I try to be, but this lot are strict with me.'

'Ya got ta have some fun on this job. It can boggle ya brain after a while,' Amy replies, pouring herself her third glass of wine. If we don't make our move pretty quickly she could be too drunk to complete the mission.

'That's the problem with these lot. They sometimes have too much fun,' I tell her.

Steph is rummaging in her bag, and the next time I glance at her she's pulled out a pair of really small binoculars to check on the target.'

'Stephanie! What are you doing, you tool?' I ask her in alarm.

'I can't bloody see, I told you. I'm just checking him out! He's alright actually. Not amazing, but OK.' She puts the binoculars back in her bag.

'You lot really are just investigators, aren't ya?' Amy is clearly stating the obvious here.

After twenty minutes, the target and his chums up sticks and leave for the next bar, taking their groupies with them. In total we're now following about fifteen people: the target with five of his friends, and the rest of them girls aged between eighteen and twenty. This situation doesn't look very promising, if I'm being honest.

In the next bar they head to another VIP section, but we find seating much closer. This time Steph and I can actually see what is going on.

We spend the next half hour waiting, then one of his friends heads for the toilet.

'Follow him,' I hiss at Steph, who does exactly as she is told, jumping down from her perch.

Fifteen minutes later I realise that Steph hasn't come back from following him. I look around but can't see her. Panic grips the pit of my stomach. Just as I'm reaching into my bag for my phone, I spot her out of the corner of my eye. She's at the bar, having a drink with the target's friend.

'How the bloody hell did she do that?' I ask Jess and Amy.

'She's a clever worker, that one. A certain career in this line of work.' Amy looks on approvingly.

'Shit, she's walking over here. Look casual,' Jess says.

'We are casual!' I tell her, but she's flapping around in her handbag. Where did my cool, calm detective go?

'Ladies, this is Charles.' Steph is at the table and introducing us to her new friend.

'Hi, Charles,' I say, giving a very dumb wave.

'Hello, Charles.' Jess has adopted a posh accent, the weirdo!

'Hi, Charles. I'm Amy.' She offers her hand, which he takes and kisses graciously. Blimey.

'Ladies, Stephanie here is rather intriguing me. Would you care to join us for some champagne at our table?' Charles invites us.

'Love to, darl!' says Amy.

We all stand up and follow him over to the table.

'Gentlemen, this is Stephanie. I'm sorry, I don't think I caught all your names.' He looks at us for clues.

Steph leaps in. 'This is Amy, Fiona [pointing at Jess] and Tanya [pointing at me].' Is she serious? Could she not have given us cool names? It's going to be fun trying to remember!

We all say our hellos and take seats among the men, with the groupies behind us. This is the first time I've been able to view our target up close. He's a dashing gentleman type. If we'd met them all in the middle of Chelsea, I wouldn't have been surprised. He has short dark hair, and lots of perfectly shaped stubble. His eyes are very brown and he almost looks like a Middle Eastern prince. His friends all have similar appearances. It's not very difficult to see how they attracted such a vast gaggle of groupies – apart from the fact that they're quaffing champagne, and doling it out freely to anyone who pays them ten seconds of interest.

After twenty minutes we know them all. Our target has been introduced to us. We know he's a computer programmer, but he's telling us that he's the owner of a communications company. Clearly we're not the only ones telling fibs tonight. As designated driver I won't touch any of the champagne they keep offering up, and neither does Steph. We're both too sensible to drink on the job. Amy does, however, and so does our lovely Jess – much to my disapproval.

His friends say they're entrepreneurs and company directors. Well, that's fine by us, because tonight I'm a fashion buyer for one of the UK's largest luxury clothing websites, Steph is a fashion designer for an Internet company, and Jess has her own boutique in central Manchester. What kind of crazy world are we living in?

Amy is, however, simply Amy, and tops us all off. Apparently she left our fashion school to start a career in acting. According to her, she's been an extra in a Brad Pitt film in the US and spent the past year living in New York to make her 'dreams come true'. We all know it's a pack of lies, but at least she's only elaborated on her 'acting' career – not the other one.

The groupies still aren't leaving, and I'm hoping and praying one of them does something with the target. Two of them do appear to have thrown themselves at him, and he has been flirtatious in return. He certainly comes across as the type of character our client described. He's smooth, and could be described as arrogant. According to our client, if we throw ourselves at him, there's no way we'll be turned down.

Over an hour passes. Jess and Amy have nearly drunk a bottle of the free champagne. One of the gentlemen asks if we want to go back to one of their houses for a pool party. When Jess tells him we have no swimming attire, he proceeds to tell us it's a 'naked pool party' only. Er, no thanks. Think we'll make our excuses when it gets to that point.

'I'm goin' ta wind this up now,' Amy leans over and whispers to me.

I nod at her and sit back in my chair, bracing myself like I'm strapped into an aeroplane seat ready for take off.

Amy sits at the side of the target and places her hand on his leg. I feel sick. My camera is ready to go, though. Tonight I'm filming everything with the video camera on my phone, and there's also a tiny one sewn into my handbag. I've placed a pen on the table out of sight, which could capture the audio, but really we only want the video.

Amy's laughing and joking, virtually falling in his lap. I feel sicker. Steph is staring at her aghast. She keeps glancing at me because she can sense how uncomfortable I am.

Amy is asking about his life story: where he comes from, what he does, if he has a girlfriend. He's telling the absolute truth about all of it – well, apart from the occupation bit. He tells Amy about his girlfriend. Amy says if he wants to go back to her house, she won't tell his girlfriend. He laughs, but really he's just politely saying no. She asks if he will be going to the pool party, but he says it's not his thing and he finds it degrading for all concerned. Amy tells him that she too has a boyfriend, but a bit of sexual fun never hurt anyone. I'm literally wincing, as if I'm in actual pain hearing all this. He laughs again, but tells her that her (fictitious) boyfriend wouldn't like it. She tells him that her (fictitious) boyfriend cheats all the time, and thinks she doesn't know. Target tells her how sad that must be for her, and he genuinely seems sad. Amy tells him she's about to break off her (fictitious) relationship, and he tells her he wants to marry his girlfriend.

This has gone far enough. Amy is flirting outrageously, and he is rebuffing every single advance. Jess and Steph are both as engrossed in the conversation as I am, but we need to end this now. He's faithful. He's done nothing all night long to suggest otherwise. Groupies have fawned over him. His friends have talked about naked pool parties, but he doesn't care. He's not said one word to lead anyone on and he's not a cheater. I know. I can tell. This man is a gentleman, just on a night out having fun.

'Right, Amy, let's go,' I announce, standing up. 'Gentlemen, it's been a pleasure. Thank you very much for your hospitality.'

'Yes, and enjoy the pool party,' says Jess, as both she and Steph step out of the VIP section with me.

'But ladies, I'm only gettin' started,' Amy says, clearly not getting the hint.

'We're going to the next bar,' I tell her. Surely she'll understand this is my signal to stop.

'Never flaming thought about code words, did we?' Jess mutters, shuffling her feet and looking at the floor.

'Come on,' I tell them both and walk towards the door. Amy and the target are still in view. We watch her swing her leg over the target's leg, grab hold of his face and kiss him.

'You have got to be kidding me,' I say, utterly furious.

'Oh my God!' Steph has her hand over her mouth and looks gobsmacked. 'This is just awful. There's no way he's interested in her. Or any of us, for that matter.'

As we stand at the entrance watching, the target throws Amy right off him, gets to his feet and storms off.

'YES!' cries Jess. 'Good man!' He's stomping towards us to reach the exit.

'Your friend is a lunatic,' he says furiously as he barges past us and through the door. We watch Amy regain her composure.

'Screw her,' I say, and charge through the exit behind him. Steph and Jess follow.

'What are we doing?' Jess asks, running behind me as fast as her stilettos will carry her.

'Leaving,' I say, stropping like I've not stropped in a long time.

'What are we doing about Amy?' Steph asks.

'She can go to hell for all I care. That was out of order.'

Jess and Steph agree with me. We dive into the car and speed past the bar. Amy is standing outside looking for us but I don't care. She's been paid in advance so I don't owe her anything more. We leave her there, on the pavement. Where she belongs.

*   *   *

A few days later and we're back at my place having a debrief about recent events.

'We're never doing anything like that ever again,' I tell them both.

'What did you tell the client?' Jess asks.

'I sent him a full transcript of the conversation our target had with Amy, and told him no matter how hard we tried he simply wasn't interested and rebuffed any advances.'

'Well, that's not a lie,' Steph says.

'It's the absolute truth. He may have wanted us to set him up for a fall, but that's not what honey trapping is. Or at least it's not what it should be.'

'How do you mean?'

'From now on, we're not taking part in anything like that. Here's my idea.' I hand them both a sheet of paper with the new honey trapping guidelines. 'In basic terms, I've developed an ethical way of honey trapping. This type of work is supposed to test if someone is faithful or not. That's all. First of all, we're only having staff work on jobs if they are a decent match for the target. For example, no page three models employed to honey trap a sixty-year-old man. It has to be a person who they would naturally be paired with if they were a real couple, both in looks and characteristics.'

'Sounds fair.'

'There will be no kissing or physical contact of any kind. None whatsoever. Our staff can flirt, and hint they may be interested in the person but that is as far as it goes.'

'Nice thinking.' Both ladies are nodding in agreement.

'What we want to achieve at our first meeting with the target is a phone number, email address or a social media contact. We want to build up a rapport with the person over a period of time. A kiss one night in a bar while drunk proves absolutely nothing. We want to get as much information as we possibly can out of the person. Finally, after a couple of weeks of rapport building by online honey trapping, we arrange a further date. We can hint that we want to go to bed with them when we arrange the date. If the target then agrees, and turns up, we will be there to record the evidence in photos and video. They can't explain it away. It proves beyond any doubt that the target intended to be unfaithful.'

'You're the boss,' Jess says laughing.

'Sounds sensible,' Steph agrees.

'Traditional honey trapping is entrapment, and we're not going to be a part of that. We have too many morals and ethics to let this one side of the work get in our way. We'll call our version ethical honey trapping.'

Finally my dilemma of the past few weeks has fallen into place. Problems and situations will arise in this job that I don't like. They may make me question the industry and even myself at times. What's important, though, is that we work on them and find a way round them. Make it so that we feel comfortable – I never again want to find myself in a situation like I was in last week. If we just talk about problems and find a way through them, I hope we'll be OK in the end.

TRANSSEXUALS R US ... GOD HELP ME!

_____

I'm driving on the motorway, singing my heart out to the Spice Girls. It's a revival moment! Generally I don't like them very much, although I was hugely into the madness that happened round the world when they first broke on the scene. I've pretty much not listened to them since, but right now, on the M6 on the way to the Lake District, I'm singing my heart right out. The phone is in its holder, and I'm thinking it's been quiet for the past day or two. And then it rings with the _Murder, She Wrote_ theme tune! Jess Fletcher is my favourite TV spy! Spice Girls go off, and as the phone is in its hands-free holder (because I'm exceptionally law-abiding), I press the answer button.

'Hellooo,' I say in a sing-song voice, still under the influence of the Spice Girls. Oops.

'Hi. Er, I have a problem that I need to speak with someone about.' It's a man and, from his worried tone of voice, clearly a customer.

'Well, you can talk to me if you want.' I'm trying to stay upbeat. I always find that if you are upbeat you get off to a better start, rather than begin a depression-fest right from the outset.

'OK, well, I've been trying to divorce my husband for some time now.' (Is this my first ever gay customer? Certainly sounds like it might be!) 'He's a very crafty man, very crafty.' Aren't they all? I'm dying to interject, but no – I refrain. 'He hides his assets from me, not that we can find him to have his assets hidden, though. My solicitor has been trying to track him down for two years but – one thing and another – she can't locate him.'

'All right, that's no problem. I'll need more factual information, but you can give me that later on,' I tell him, thinking it sounds a very easy job.

'He took thousands of pounds from me. By way of my bank accounts, my car and other things that I won't go into. Basically, if we find him I can get a decent amount back. I can't wait any longer, though – money is really tight and my solicitor is costing a small fortune. I need this dealing with quickly. We're based in the Scottish Highlands so it's not so easy for us to find him.'

'I'm sure we can do something, and we always try to be affordable. Where do you think he is?'

'His home town is London, but last I heard he was located in Sydney.'

All of a sudden, visions of the perfect job spring to mind. Sandy beaches, surfing and sipping cocktails in front of the Opera House. I'll take a trip to Sydney to find this geezer!

'However, I'm almost 100 per cent certain we're being conned on the Sydney front.' And so the bubble pops! 'He'll be in London, but whereabouts I don't know.'

'That's no problem. What has your solicitor done to find him, exactly?'

'I know she's run lots of legal checks on him. His bank accounts are there, but with no money in. He rents an apartment, but we can't find a lease. There's no trace of him in the UK. He has no property here, and he isn't registered on the electoral roll.'

'Do you think he may have married again?' I'm thinking it would be very easy to find him if I could trace a recent marriage certificate.

'I do wonder if he has, but I'm not sure to be honest. If he has married again, it could be to a woman or a man. I heard he had a boyfriend from Sydney, whom he dumped a few months ago, but since then he's shacked up with another one.'

Obviously the reason why he was there. 'It's making a bit more sense now.' I'm thinking that I've got no idea how on earth we are going to find this man. There's not even a small thread of information I can cling onto. 'How involved in the gay scene is he?' I ask him, trying to find just a snippet of information.

'Oh, he loves it. At one time he was incredibly butch, but now he is ridiculously feminine.'

Interesting! Sounds like if we do find him, it will be a fun case.

'OK, you're going to have to leave it with me. I'll charge you a one-off fee for a week's worth of investigation. It's only going to be a couple of hundred pounds, because it's highly possible we're not going to find him. If we don't, you won't get your money back. But either way, it will be cheap. I'm going to give it some thought, chat to a few of the girls, and if we can't come up with a slight lead, or at least an idea of how to find him, I'll let you know and you can ask other people to do the job. I don't want to take your money with no hope of finding him.' I feel secretly worried that there's no hope – but yet there's a slight glimmer. A gut instinct tells me I can do something, somehow.

'Of course, that sounds fair to me.'

'Great. I'll give you a call later this evening, if that's OK?' He agrees.

By the end of our chat, I'm pulling up outside my house in God's Waiting Room. Today, the residents are out in force tending their flowerbeds. I feel bizarrely settled and happy surrounded by older people. Maybe in a former life I looked after them or something. I have a chat over the shrubs with the next-door neighbour, as usual about the weather and not much else. I smile politely, phone and laptop under my arm, and go inside. Kettle gets flicked on, and I take my seat at the desk overlooking the front garden.

Next I pick up the phone and ring Jess. I need to explain the situation to her and see what she thinks. My mind is all cloudy and fuzzy. I don't seem to be able to see the light in this case, but I do believe it's there. I outline the story to her, and she comes up with a thought.

'It's Friday today. We have to be in London for a job next week. So, let's get down there and start a little earlier!'

We'll head for Soho, the main gay area of London, because our client has mentioned a couple of bars he thinks he frequents. It's a huge long shot, but at the end of the day, what else do we have to go on? May as well give it a go, and if it fails at least we're in for a good night out! Neither of us needs much convincing to go and party under the pretext of working.

I arrange to pick up Jess at 6pm and ring back my client, whose name, by the way, is Timothy, or Timmy as he likes to be known.

'Timmy. This may sound bizarre, but we're going to London tonight. If he is heavily involved in the gay scene, you just never know,' I tell him, wondering if I'm trying to convince him or myself. 'I'm not charging you, it's just us trying to get a lead.'

'Alright, that's very good of you. Thank you.' He sounds impressed, but I'm thinking we sound really unprofessional with this ridiculous stab in the dark.

'I just need you to email me a picture, if you can?' I ask. Timmy agrees. While I'm waiting for the email wind-breaking alert noise I dive into the wardrobe to find a wonderful, fabulously sparkly outfit for the evening. Should make me fit right in!

★   ★   ★

Dressed up to the nines and armed with the picture, I pick up Jess from her house. She's already started on a bottle of wine, and gets in the car with bottle and glass in hand. She's the only person I let drink on the job. Mainly because she's been with me from the beginning; but also she isn't getting paid for this jaunt. Jess isn't just an employee – she's my friend and I trust her to remain professional!

'*Buongiorno!*' Now Jess is pinching my phrases. She falls into the car, sloshing wine everywhere, dressed in an equally spangly outfit.

'Do you think people will assume we're gay lovers?' I ask her.

'Highly possible. I'll be your gay lover for one evening.' She's very cheerful tonight!

We make our way to the train station, and spend forever faffing around, almost missing our train. Usually I include 'faffing' time in our schedules, but tonight I've made an over-sight due to all the rushing. Finally, two hours (and a bottle of wine for Jess) later, we have arrived in the capital. Armed and ready.

We collect our rental car and make our way to Soho, only to find it's a nightmare for parking. I eventually decide to park illegally on some double yellows. Parking tickets are one of my favourite collections, after all, and we're not planning on hanging around long enough to get towed!

We stomp our way down the street, sparkly, spangly and in huge high heels that make us wobble the entire way. We are as far from the stereotypical detectives as you can get: we're dizzy by name and by nature!

Our first stop is a bar that we're told is the new 'in' place to be. Contemporary, with a twist, it's cool but still with a slightly cheesy edge to it, and full of men!

We arrive quite early, mainly so it's easier to acclimatise ourselves to it. The other reason being that we can be lovely and friendly with the bar staff, and they may give us more information. We sit for an hour or so, just surveying the clien-tele. We should leave soon and check out other places, to make us feel we're serving more of a purpose than just prop-ping up a bar. We can't see anyone who matches our target's description. It would be incredible if we did. From the infor-mation we've been given by Timmy, he is short. Five foot nine, with a very broad, butch frame, dark hair that's down to his shoulders and perma-tanned (apparently he uses sunbeds). His face is lined (mainly due to the sunbeds, I expect).

I'm sat at the end of the bar, propped on a stool with my chin resting on my fist. I'm squinting, too, because as usual I've forgotten to bring my glasses and can hardly see the faces of people at the end of the bar. Jess is chatting away, laughing and giggling with the barman while holding some mad-looking cocktail. It's highly possible she's drunk by this point. I'm a little irritated with myself, because it's not going as I want. I stand up and make my way towards her, putting on my 'happy face'.

'Bec,' says Jess, 'come meet … er … What's your name? Surgio?'

'Ser-gio!' the barman says, smiling.

'Ser-gio!' she repeats. 'Ah yes, Surgio is that meerkat off the telly!'

'Hi, Sergio,' I say, shaking his hand. 'Is she bothering you?'

'No, no, we've been having a thrilling conversation. Jess is a football expert,' he says, gesturing towards her with a huge smile. Jess nods at him with a grin on her face, and then takes another sip of her drink. Sergio is part Italian, I guess, but he has a perfect English accent. I would ask why but I actually can't be bothered.

'What are you two straight girls doing here this fine evening?' He's very charming, clearly under Jess's down-to-earth spell.

'What on earth makes you think we're straight?' I ask, laughing.

'She's my life partner!' Jess nods.

'All right, all right, now what are you really doing here?' he asks again, rolling his eyes. We're clearly not very good at acting tonight.

'I'm trying to find my mum's long-lost brother,' I tell him.

'Oh, really? Here?' He sounds surprised.

'Yes, he came out a few years ago. It's a long shot, to be fair, but I'll literally do anything for my mum. And at her age, a night out in Soho isn't exactly appropriate.'

Now he looks sympathetic. 'Aw, that's really sweet,' he says with a half-smile, head on one side. Head on one side always means some version of sympathy. He's falling under the spell; maybe our acting is going better than I thought.

'Show him your picture!' Jess suggests. 'He may know him!'

'Oh yes! Good idea.' I fish in my bag for the picture and hand it over.

'Now then,' he says, giving the picture a strange look.

'Do you know him?' I ask, thinking there's some hope there.

'He does look familiar, you know, but if it's who I think it is they're not like this any more.'

Jess and I look at each other, very confused. 'How do you mean?'

'Well, I could be really wrong, but it's the tan and the lines on his face.' Sergio is staring at the picture.

'Oh go on. Tell us. We need something to go on. It's worth a shot.' I'm almost pleading.

'He looks a lot like a transsexual who comes in here all the time. I mean, literally every week, three times a week. You know, one of the regulars.'

I feel a bit shocked, and part of me thinks 'no chance'. Yet, if there's one thing this job has taught me, it's to expect the unexpected.

'Go on …' Jess looks stumped.

'He's been coming in for a few months. Lived in Sydney before that – he's got a boyfriend over there who's always with him.' Oh my God! Is this it?

'What else do you know?' I'm trying not to sound desperate, but it's all fitting in.

'I don't really want to say, if it's your mother's brother. Like I say, I could be wrong. More I look at the picture, though, the more I think I'm not.' He's watching us sympathetically. Jess's jaw is on the floor!

'Trust me. Mum knows what he's like. She still loves him anyway. Don't worry, you're being a massive help,' I say, smiling at him while nudging Jess with my foot under the table. Her jaw shuts and she gulps.

'The rumour, and it is just a rumour, is that he's working as a transsexual prostitute.'

WOW! Didn't expect that. 'Yep, that sounds like him.' Nodding as I say it. Not a clue if it is him, but the Sydney connection seems a clue so we may as well go along with this and see what else we find out.

'Really? Oh good, happy I've been some help, then!' Sergio says, looking pleased with himself.

'Huge help. Really, I mean that. You've been wonderful.' Jess is gathering her things, and we're getting ready to leave. 'Just a thought,' I say to Sergio. 'If he's now a woman, he won't still be called Jack, will he?'

'No, no. That person goes by the name of Jackie. That sounds right, though, doesn't it? Jack to Jackie.' Sergio thinks it's funny.

'Oh, that certainly sounds right,' I giggle. We offer our goodbyes and leave. Sergio has no idea how much help he has just been.

The night air is cold when we leave, but our elation is keeping us warm. We link arms and cling together, tramping our way back down the streets. We hang around the area a while longer in the hope of seeing him, but nothing. I'm not too bothered – we've got something to go on. We trot back to the car. Jess is wasted, and I take her to our hotel.

As soon as we're in our room I hit the laptop and start Googling 'Jackie Vernon', 'Vernon' being his previous surname. Nothing. 'Transsexuals, London' I search. 'Transsexual prostitutes, London'. Lots of websites come up, and I spend ages trailing through them – but he's not on any of them. I lie back on the bed, sparkly outfit and heels still on. I stare at the ceiling, hoping something will come to me. I've got a lead, but I'm failing. I feel strangely at peace, and drift off into a deep sleep, laptop still on my knees …

★   ★   ★

It's 10am and I wake with a start – and I don't mean because of Jess in the bed next to me snoring like Thomas the Tank Engine. I've got it.

Like I'd never been asleep, I pull the laptop back onto my knee and Google: 'Jackie transsexual London'. A website comes up. 'This site contains explicit content. Please click "Continue" if you are over eighteen.' I click it quickly and shut my eyes. Partly because I'm scared of what I will see, and partly because I'm scared it won't be him. If it's not, I don't know what else to do.

The first page contains a picture of an over-inflated (collagen-injected) pair of lips, wrapped around a gentleman's manly parts. I have an overwhelming urge to throw up, but I swallow it down. I then hit the 'About Jackie' page … IT'S HIM! The laptop falls to the floor as I jump up, screaming and doing a fancy little dance around the bedroom. Jess begins to stir. I'm spinning around in my bare feet and gold sequin dress (heels must have been kicked off while I was asleep). 'It's him, it's him, it's him, it's him!' I sing, spinning, and dancing a lot like a leprechaun. 'Ahhh!' I scream, clenching my fists in a ball before sitting back on the bed and getting the laptop back, ready to investigate some more.

'Him! Where?' Jess sits bolt upright in bed looking around as if she thinks he's just walked into the room.

'No, silly. Here, on the computer. Look,' I say, spinning the laptop around on my knee so she can see. She screams, half-horrified, half-happy. That's before she falls back onto the bed, holding her head.

I read all about Jackie, who classes himself as 'transgender'. I basically grasp this means that he acts and lives like a woman, but still has man bits. He's in London – not that there's an address. There is a description of his location though, and the website tells me that it isn't far from Soho. I look at the gallery page, but after ten seconds I run to the bathroom and literally am sick. The pictures are too much. Jackie is performing sex acts on men – lots of them – and it's extreme stuff. It shows Jackie in all his glory. He is indeed short and very masculine, but his breasts are simply massive, and have a very 'stuck on' appearance. Bad surgeon clearly. The lips are ridiculous – he must buy collagen by the bucket-load. He has dark hair extensions down to his waist but you can see where the real hair ends, just below his ears. I've never seen more fake-look-ing extensions, and that's saying something ... I live in Manchester, for goodness' sake!

He must still have a passion for sunbeds, as the lines on his face are dreadful. I'd have thought that when he was purchas-ing his vast quantities of collagen, he'd do the same with Botox! His skin is paper-thin. For want of a better description, there's never been a more fake-looking woman. It's screamingly obvious he's a man, and the pictures of his man bits and fake boobs – all on show – confirm this. I have clearly lived a very sheltered life. You hear of people like this, but you don't believe they actually exist.

I pick up the phone and tell Timmy what we've found out. 'Oh, that sounds like him all right. It's so embarrassing,' he tells me. 'I can't believe I was ever married to him. Do you think you'll be able to find him now?'

'I do. We still have a long way to go, but this is the lead I was wanting. One way or another, I'm sure we can find him. It just may not be very conventional detective work.' Timmy is happy. He pays with his card over the phone, and I ring Steph to tell her what's happened.

Next I show Jess the pictures of Jackie/Jack, in all her/his glory. I think I'm going to have to call him Jackie; that's the correct thing to do. Jess is equally as disturbed, but we crack on regardless. (Finally I've had a shower and changed out of last night's party gear.) I press the contact button on the website and send an email saying that I think she's really hot and I'd like to meet up. Yuck! Next I run various traces on Jackie, but nothing comes back; we both sit staring at the pictures. Jess is now dressed in a black outfit. I'm half-waiting for her to pull out sunglasses, even though we're indoors. She's not looking her most glam right now, it has to be said.

'If we stare a bit harder, it will come to us,' I say.

'It will …' she says, not even realising she's talking to me. We're both still adjusting to this new situation.

'Here's a thought – huge long shot, though. Look at the pictures. They're all taken in what looks like a property that, if I'm not mistaken, is some version of a converted schoolhouse, or a character building of some kind. It has a roof terrace overlooking a modern office building, next to what looks like a Georgian building, and it's on the banks of a river which must be the Thames. The rooms have high ceilings and one has an original spiral staircase that I'm guessing is a feature they've had to retain for planning reasons. The seats under the windows look like pews.'

'So we're really, officially, going to start looking for needles in haystacks now?' Jess says, still staring at the computer.

'Possibly, but I'm going to give this a go.' I regain control of the computer and start hitting estate agents' websites, searching for character riverside properties for sale. Over 250! Jess leaves for a bit while I begin to look through every single listing. I quickly realise my search needs to be more concentrated. I look for property that could potentially be in an old school, warehouse or factory on the banks of the Thames. I soon narrow it down to four apartment blocks that look like possible locations.

I ring the estate agent handling at least one apartment in each block and make viewing appointments for the following day. There could also be other blocks in the area that don't have apartments for sale, but I'll give it a go. Pretending to be a buyer is the only way you get to nose around these places and it's the only action I can take considering that Jackie has very rudely not replied to my email. I spend the rest of the day taking in some sights, while Jess recovers from the night before. I wholeheartedly decide that this is the very last time she's allowed to drink on a job. Her sheepish manner suggests she knows this already.

The next morning we go to view the apartments. They're all spaced a couple of hours apart, so we have time to check out each block properly. We're late, as usual! I pull up in front of the block just as I see the estate agent leaving. Jess jumps out of the car while it's almost still moving.

'Stop!' she shouts, flashing her winning smile. 'Sorry we're so late.' The gentleman is around twenty-five, young and semi good-looking, and he can't resist her charm. I also jump out of the car, abandoning it on the double yellow lines outside. I simply don't have time to find a legal space.

I've already instructed Jess to remember the code the agent puts into the front door, so that we can let ourselves back in. If he uses a key we're in trouble. Sure enough, he does it in full view, without trying to hide it from us. Very easy – thank you very much! As we go up in the lift, we ask how safe the building is. We'd noticed some cameras outside, and say it's a bit worrying. What are the residents like?

'I'm not too sure, to be honest. We sell a lot out of this building but we don't have any problems that we know of.' Useless agent, as per usual.

'Great. Do you know how many apartments are in here?' I ask.

'I think about thirty. Is it for yourselves?' he asks.

'No, we buy to rent out. Thinking this one will get a good rental value, being so central,' Jess says.

'It will, actually. Anyway, here we go,' and he lets us in. We mooch around, asking all the usual pointless questions. The guy who currently rents the house is in, but is entirely useless. We press him on the other residents, and he tells us that he keeps himself to himself and that's it. Boring. We thank the agent for his time and he lets us out. We wait around the corner, watching him leave. Thankfully our car hasn't got a ticket, so I move it now we have a bit more time. Once it's safely out of the way we go back to the building. It's then I notice a Georgian building that looks like the one next door to the apartment in Jackie's website. This could be the one! Luckily someone is just leaving as we reach the door, and he holds it open for us to go back inside, so we don't even have to use the code (which I suspect may be illegal …).

We hurry around as quickly as our heels will take us, trying to find the letter boxes. I've lived in apartment blocks before, and the letter boxes can generally fit a hand inside. Not that we would take the mail, of course, but simply to see who it's meant for and put it back. But when we find the letter boxes here, we discover that they're the world's most secure system! Hardly anything more than a letter will fit through the gap. Letter-box trick is not an option!

'Well, that was worth it,' Jess says sarcastically.

'Hush up,' I tell her. 'Let's start knocking on doors. We'll start at the top and work our way down. Try one apartment on each floor, and if it doesn't work we'll come back tomorrow and try another.' This could all be very much a long shot, but we have to try. Lots of time and effort is going into this, but my gut instinct is saying it's highly possible we'll be rewarded.

'Good plan.' We arrive on the top floor.

'Right, pick a door,' Jess says. These doors are not very normal. Some are painted pink, some have glitter on. Could this indicate gay residents? Or young children? 'This one will do,' I say, walking up to one that's covered in silver sparkles. Jess knocks.

'Hello. We've come to view the apartment,' she says to the woman who answers.

'Sorry, I think you have the wrong one,' she tells us.

'Oh, really? Number forty, yes?' I ask.

'No, this is sixty. You want the floor below.'

'Oh, of course,' I say, giggling and pointing at the door number.

'Sorry, we're so dizzy!' Jess apologises.

We say goodbye and take the lift down to the next floor.

Knock, knock. This time on a normal-looking door. A guy no older than nineteen comes to the door in his dressing gown, which is open to the waist.

'Ooooh, hellooooo,' he says in a very feminine voice, pulling his dressing gown closed.

'Sorry, we've come to view your apartment,' I say.

'What? Oh dear, that's today?' he frowns.

'Er, yes – have we come at a bad time?' Jess asks.

'I think we may have the time wrong,' I tell them both.

'No, no, it's fine, luvvies.' Poor kid.

'You are with Premier Estates, aren't you?' I ask him.

'Yes!' What flaming chance is that! We've picked a flat that is for sale, and with an agent I named off the top of my head.

'Oh, don't worry, we'll come back later,' Jess says.

'No, honestly, come on in. It's my fault. I'm just putting the kettle on. Would you like one?' He walks back inside, leaving the door open for us to follow. We look at each other and I pull a face that's a cross between 'uh oh' and 'what do we do?' We follow inside, and view the boy's apartment. We tell him it's very nice and that we'll ring the agent later. Oops.

We come out and rush for the lift, shaking our heads when safely inside.

'What are we doing?' Jess exclaims.

'Don't know, but let's do it again.' I tell her.

Next floor. I pick a door that's electric pink all over, with an ultra-lilac doormat. Very strange. What's even more strange is the three locks, two security cameras and a peep-hole. Clearly an odd resident with something to hide. We knock.

'Hello,' says a gruff voice from behind the door.

'Hi. We've come to view the apartment.'

'Helloooooooooo,' says the man, whose voice has suddenly gone very high-pitched, and he swings the door wide open.

And we come face to face with … Jackie!

'Hi!!!' I say, suddenly very elated.

'I'm afraid my home isn't for sale, darlings.' I look at Jess who is stood next to me with a beaming smile on her face.

'What? Oh my goodness. I'm so sorry,' I tell Jackie, still glowing with sheer happiness. He is a very jolly transsexual. 'We must have the wrong one.'

'I am open to offers, though,' he says in a happy, inviting and very dodgy tone! We laugh and look at each other. Jackie laughs, we all laugh.

'You are so dizzy,' Jess says, looking at me in mock exasperation.

'I really am,' I say. 'I'm so sorry to have bothered you!'

'Any time, darlings, any time,' Jackie says, shutting the door. We turn around, very pleased with ourselves, and get back into the lift. What follows is another very fancy leprechaun-style dance. This time it's the two of us, spinning, dancing, in a very small lift.

We get in the car, and clear off into the centre of town for lunch. Easy job.

Once we're sitting in a lovely little Italian restaurant, I telephone Timmy and tell him the good news. He is nothing short of thrilled, as are we. It's such an amazing feeling when it goes so right – especially when all the odds were against us.

Back at the hotel a few hours later, I start running all my usual checks on Jackie. Having his address opens up a whole new world of possible finds. What transpires after a hard day's work is that he is indeed a very, very dodgy character.

He's set up a car company, with his friend as the director. His house is registered to the company as an office, therefore he thinks he is untouchable. If it was in his name his ex could take a share, if not the whole thing. He also has other houses dotted around the country that he's renting out. He spends three months in Sydney during the summer – for what reason is anyone's guess. Don't ask me how I found all this out. I need to retain some secrets. It wasn't especially hard though. We pass over all the information to Timmy, who sends it on to his solicitor to see if any of his assets can be seized.

'One last thing,' says Timmy, when I've relayed all the information. 'He likes very nice cars. Whatever he is driving will be worth quite a bit. Do you think you can find out what he's got?'

While we were viewing the apartment the first time, the agent did show us the garage in the basement. There were only about ten cars, but one stood out. An Aston Martin. I had a hunch. We'd taken pictures and had the registration of said car, but you can only ask the DVLA to give you the owner's information if you have a judgment against the person whose car you believe it is. At this point, Timmy didn't have a judgment.

We make another appointment to view the apartment, but ask if we can see the owner instead of the boy who's renting, to answer some of our questions. The agency confirms that the owner is happy to meet us.

We return with agent and owner, and once again do our best acting, asking her even more pointless questions than we did the first time. We go down to the basement, and stand in front of the Aston Martin.

'Wow, I really love this car!' I say, looking at it longingly.

'Yes, it is rather lovely, isn't it?' says the apartment owner.

'Do you know who it belongs to?' I ask.

'Yes. It's er, Jack's. Or Jackie's. Whatever he wants to call himself this week!' she says, with a slight look of disapproval.

'What do you mean?' Jess asks in all innocence.

'Well, it's neither a he nor a she! You know, one of those transsexual types,' and in unison Jess and I sigh 'Aaahhhhhhhhhh,' and look away, secretly smiling to ourselves and walking towards the lift.

'Shall we go?' I look at Jess.

'We shall!' she replies with a huge grin.

★   ★   ★

Jackie had slipped up: the car was the one thing registered in his own name, and he was made to declare it to Timmy's solicitor. The last I heard, Timmy was still battling for the rest of his assets and holding out hope of getting his car. That will be a very lengthy process.

Timmy's solicitor had spent two years trying to find Jackie. It took us in total five days, and a pittance of a wage. I love equipment, and how easy our life is made by the Internet, but we solved this case with sheer intuition. Good, old-fashioned investigation work. I did feel a huge sense of victory. Although I am irritated that Jackie never replied to my email. I'm normally pretty convincing when I'm pretending to be other people, but maybe there was something in my tone that didn't sound the way a person seeking the services of a transsexual prostitute would sound. It's not an area in which I have a huge amount of experience!

Jackie is a likeable character, with a very cheery disposition. You could tell he is fun and amusing to be around. But what most people who come across him won't know about is his seedy lifestyle, that shocking website and the way he has ripped off his own husband. It taught me a lesson, though – just when you think you know it all and you can't be shocked any more, something even more crazy and bizarre will come along to surprise you.

But at least we can stamp this one 'case closed'!

SAYING GOODBYE
TO THE PAST

Houston, we have a problem. I know most people will regard my problem as pathetic but here it is … I'm 'too' happy. I mean, what muppet actually says that? I was talking to a friend about it the other day and she made it very clear she thought I was stupid. Lots of people would love to be in my situation and be 'too happy', but I'm scared.

It's Ben. I literally can't fault the man. Three months into the relationship, there's not one tiny issue with him. I pine for him all the time when we're apart, and we never argue. We don't even bicker. He has no problem with anything I say, and fully supports everything I want to do. Don't get me wrong. He's not soft; he's a real man's man. But we're too compatible. When we clash there's going to be one almighty explosion.

I've always had issues with good guys. I'm the classic girl who wants a bad boy. I wholeheartedly believe it's bred into us. Take Paris as proof. The child is only a few years old, and the sum total of her world knowledge is as follows: *Peppa Pig* is cool, Granddad is her best friend, sweeties make everything OK and drawing on walls is much more fun than drawing on paper! Highly innocent, not yet in any way, shape or form corrupted by society. So … here is where she proves my theory. Every day for the past year I've heard how Tom and James are the 'naughty' boys in class at nursery. Really naughty – she gets very mad with them. They squirt everyone with water, Tom is always digging up the school's plants and James never listens to the teachers. Imagine my horror when Paris swanned in from school a couple of days ago to tell me … 'I've decided I love Tom!' THAT is the proof. It's bred into all females: we love bad boys! It's not a lifestyle choice, it's just the way we are! And I'm no exception.

Ben is quite literally too good, and I'm terrified. I struggle to put it all into words. I know this is going to go wrong; this relationship cannot possibly run the distance. I'm totally falling for him, but I can't risk getting hurt ever again. Deep down I'm scared I'm not a good person, that I'm going to hurt him, and I can't risk doing that to this amazing man.

I don't think I can ever trust anyone again. It's not just me any more either – there's Paris too. Her dad left when she was too young to understand why. She's coming through the worst finally, but it wasn't easy. Now she's almost four and much more aware of the world around her. If I introduce her to Ben, she gets attached to him and then he leaves, I don't think either of us will survive as well as we have.

Gradually all the demons in my head start muttering in my ear and my anxiety builds. I think of the way James behaved and the terrible pain it caused. I know Ben won't ever behave like that – it's me I'm worried about. I had a long-term affair behind James's back. I had succumbed once. But I'd never forgive myself if I did that to Ben and he had to go through all that pain. He's too good for me. The whole relationship is too good to be true. If he knew what I was really like, he would want out. It's not fair to continue to date him under false pretences so I need to call it off.

Ben knows there's something wrong with me. I've been distancing myself from him for days. I've flicked some kind of switch inside me and turned into a cold and calculating bitch. I figure if I irritate him enough, it will make it less painful when I end it.

'Will you come with me to that concert we were talking about in the summer?' he asks.

'We won't still be together then,' I say cruelly, and he flinches then tries to laugh it off, but I'm not in a joking mood.

'What's up with you today?' he finally asks.

That's when all my doubts and worries pour out of me. I come clean about everything I've been feeling, and tell him I can't handle the pain of another break-up. He may not have known me very long, but he knows me well enough already to rumble my plan. He guesses that I'm being cold and hard with him to make it easier on him when we break up.

'I'm not a good person,' I keep telling him. 'You're too nice for me.' I explain to him about my affair with John and the way it ended. Surely that would prove to him I'm damaged goods?

Ben isn't buying it though. He keeps telling me that he doesn't care. He already knew I'd had a long-term affair behind my husband's back, but says that he doesn't judge me for it. He understands why I did it, and believes I am a good person deep down. If my husband had been the man he was supposed to be, I'd never have done what I did.

I mean blimey – come on! I'm hardly a saint who's lost her way. How can he see such good things in me?

Next he tells me that I put myself down all the time, and I play dumb when really I'm smarter than anyone he knows. He sees through all my fakery.

I'm utterly speechless. We sit on the sofa and I just stare at his beautiful face. He stares straight back and makes me want to cry. I don't deserve this and he's making it harder than I ever imagined.

Suddenly I jump up and run upstairs to get my computer. I open up a website on which I've been writing an anonymous blog. I started it during the break-up with James as a way of releasing all the pain and hurt. I wrote down everything that was happening, all I was thinking and feeling, without holding back. I was free to be as expressive as I wanted and say whatever I liked, and so I did. I wrote warts and all. The good times, bad times and all the horrors in between. My deepest darkest thoughts were somewhere in cyberspace. I'm not the kind of person that can write things down on paper and burn it later. I needed there to be a purpose and meaning to it, so blog form it was. This is what he needs to see to know I'm not a saint who's lost her way. This will spell out what a truly horrific person I am, and that I'm fully capable of behaving the same way with him.

I go back down and hand him the computer. 'Read that!' I tell him, then go to make cups of tea. It takes Ben over two hours to read them all, and he doesn't say a word the whole time. He is utterly engrossed, and as I peep round the door I think that's probably a bad sign.

When he's finished, he closes the computer and stands up to come towards me.

'Would you like to leave now?' I ask, pointing towards the door.

'If you think for a second that's scared me away, you're wrong. I'm glad I've read it all, and thank you for sharing it with me.' He grabs hold of me with both arms, his whole six-foot-five self towering over me, and he stares into my eyes, which are filling with tears. 'You made mistakes, but we all have. There's nothing you can possibly say or do to get rid of me now. I know what your problem is. You're scared of being too happy and feel that you don't deserve what we've got. I know it's amazing – but you're an amazing person. I don't care one little bit about who you were then. I only know who you are now and I'm in love with that person. You make me the happiest I've ever been, and we've only just started. I'm going nowhere, and I can't ever see me going anywhere. So stop all this silly talk. I know you're scared, but when you get these feelings talk to me and we'll go through them together. It's why I'm here. I wouldn't change one part of you.'

Wow. He knows everything, and he's staying? Once again I'm utterly speechless.

Until this point, I hadn't realised how scarred I've been by all my experiences. It's rare to find anyone who hasn't been unfaithful. Infidelity terrifies me. I live in dread of it. I'm terrified of me doing it, and I'm terrified of him doing it. Quite ironic considering the day job. Although maybe that's why I was attracted to the job I'm in: to find out more about why people are unfaithful and gain a bit of control over the situation by honing my detection skills.

Most men would have run a mile when confronted by a hysterical woman thrusting a warts-and-all blog in their faces, and trying to break up with them for being 'too perfect', but Ben simply takes it in his stride. What did I ever do to deserve this? I can't imagine.

STAG PARTY TIMES

The *Murder, She Wrote* theme tune blasts from my phone and a Welsh voice trills, 'Ah, hell-ooww there!'

'Er, hi! How can I help?' I say, panicking slightly.

'Ay need sum-wun ter foll-oww my hus-band if poss-ible. Ay need ter know if yu can doo et, and wha' kinda prry-ces yu chaarge.'

One hand is clinging to the phone for dear life, and the other is clutching my temple. As strange as this sounds, so far we've not had any Welsh clients and I'm scared of not doing a good job if I don't understand them properly. It would be embarrassing to have to ask this person to repeat themselves a hundred times, and then getting parts wrong because I still can't understand. Thankfully, I've just managed to grasp what she's said so far.

'No problem. Basic surveillance is £40 an hour. But what do you want us to do?'

'He's go-wen furra staag paartie in Brigh-ten and Ay wanna know what 'ee gets up too,' says the lady with the super-sing-song voice.

'He's on a barge party?' I ask, really confused.

'Naw, staag paartie. *Staag.* Yer know, before a wedd-in'?'

'I'm so sorry, I'm really awful with accents,' I tell her, deciding to be honest. The lady seems really lovely, thankfully, so she just laughs. We try over the course of the next ten minutes to make some sense of our conversation. Thankfully, the lady, who I find out is called Karen, offers to email me the information. I am relieved to say the least.

After reading, digesting and finally understanding, our mission is very clear. The husband she thinks is unfaithful will be going to Brighton for a stag party and she's utterly convinced he's going to be unfaithful. We must be there to follow him. Simple.

At least this sounds like a fun job, unlike some. I've never been to Brighton. I decide Steph will be best for this one. She'll be in her element with lots of men by the seaside. When I ring to inform her, I'm met with screams and lots of excitement. I tell her we're off in three days. Just the right amount of time for her to go to the shops and plan all her outfits – bless!

I collect Steph one very sunny morning, and we head down south. It's going to be a long drive, but the other option was taking three trains and then hiring a car. That seemed a pointless and stressful plan, considering it would probably take the same amount of time. In total it takes us five and a half hours, four toilet stops, six moaning-about-men sessions (mainly by Steph, although I do have a word or two to say about the ex-husband and losing my house), three coffee breaks, two naps, one lunch break and one break to find a car charger for the laptop because it is vitally important we don't miss any more episodes of *Desperate Housewives* or Steph might go back onto the moaning-about-men sessions.

We arrive in a cold and rainy Brighton – who said it was sunny down south?

'I thought this was supposed to be the English Riviera?' Steph asks, her face pressed against the window as we drive along the front, watching the rain lash down around us.

'That's Torquay you muppet!' I tell her. She sulks.

We pull up in the car park the hotel advised us to use and have to make our way in the pouring rain to reception. All without actually knowing where we're going.

'Wait, let me sat nav,' Steph says reaching into her pocket for her phone. 'Go this way.' She's pulling a leopard-print suit-case so big that it looks like she's staying for the next three weeks, not three days.

We head out of the car park, and the rain is simply hammering down. There's no one on the streets, except us. Raindrops are bouncing off the pavement, spray is blasting off the canopies from the shops in front of us and we honestly look like we've been down a log flume. We're utterly drenched, after just a four-minute walk down a narrow street. We turn left, and the look on Steph's face tells me something's wrong.

'Er, I've gone the wrong way,' she says sheepishly, pulling her suitcase past me and back down the way we just came. I make an executive decision to keep my mouth shut, because whatever comes out wouldn't be productive.

After another two wrong turns we look like drowned rats, but we're standing outside a beautiful Victorian building on the seafront. Walking into the hotel reception, I couldn't feel more embarrassed. It's ridiculously posh, all marble floors and leather seating. The receptionist looks at us like we're tramps, and I don't blame her.

'Hello, we're here to check in.'

'Name, please,' stuffy lady asks. If that bun on her head was any tighter I think she might stop the air flow to her brain.

'Natalie Martin.' I never give our real names for check-in. You never know when a client may turn a little crazy on us and tell their other half they've hired private investigators to follow them. I've often feared it. We tell them something they don't like, they blow our cover, target comes to find us and potentially murders us. We either die or are involved in a moonlight flit. To be safe, if we use fake names, they won't find which room we're in.

'Bec, what are you doing?' Steph whispers to me with amusement, and she doesn't mean the fake name.

'I don't know. I think my subconscious felt that to make up for the fact we look like tramps I need to adopt a fake posh accent,' I reply, tilting my head at Miss Stuffy.

Stuffy is still staring at us, while printing off our check-in documents. Steph is trying to smile her out but Stuffy stares straight back, no smile. I wonder how this woman has got her job? She's supposed to be nice to customers. We've paid – well, our client has paid – nearly £200 per night for us to stay in this hotel. They're certainly no budget chain!

'First floor, turn a right out of the lift and down the corridor. Room number 215,' Stuffy says, handing over two plastic swipe cards.

Steph takes the cards. 'Awww, thank you, you've been SO helpful,' she says with a seriously over-the-top smile. She turns on her heel, grabs the leopard-print suitcase and minces off towards the lift. I follow, giggling to myself.

'Stuffy cow!' Steph remarks, hitting the button for the lift.

We walk through the door of our room and it's beautiful. Very bizarre for a stag party. I honestly expected we'd be stuck in some hell-hole of a bed and breakfast. Instead, we're in a beautiful room with a sea view. The walls are lined with parquet, the material that is normally used for flooring. For some reason these people have thrown them on the walls, and it works. Our beds are twins, thank God. Both with crisp white sheets and leather headboards.

'Yep, I'll cope,' Steph says, pulling on her complementary white dressing gown, slipping on the slippers and bouncing onto the bed.

There are lots of goodies, including a free mini-bar and movies on demand. Considering it's still pouring with rain outside, and that we've driven what feels like a million miles, we take the option to stay in. We have an early start in the morning, and the room-service menu looks pretty good.

That evening we dine on a three-course meal, in our room, at a little table overlooking the sea. I have a smoked salmon starter with a fancy garnish, roast lamb with fondant potatoes and a chocolate soufflé for dessert. When people go on about how private investigation is glamorous, we roll our eyes and insist it's totally not. These must be the moments people think of, and yes, this is most certainly glam.

After a wonderful night's sleep, our alarms go off at 6am. We have to be up super-early, just in case the boys spring a surprise on us and head off.

'What is actually going on today?' Steph asks me while battling with a pair of hair straighteners.

'I'm not exactly sure, to be honest. All I know is that they are doing some kind of activity.'

'That's it?'

I sense the uneasiness in her voice. We can never plan what's going to happen on a job. Most investigators say you should plan for every eventuality, but it's actually impossible. The wife didn't know what they're doing, so how are we to know?

'I know it's not ideal, but we'll go with the flow.'

Twenty minutes later and we've finished preparing ourselves for the day. It's vitally important at this early stage in the three-day mission that we're not seen. In the hotel it doesn't matter so much. At the end of the day, when you're staying in a hotel you bump into people all the time. But if you then see the same people everywhere you go throughout the town, it gets suspicious. We'll try our best to blend in this morning, but after that we need to keep firmly hidden. That's why I've brought Narnia with us – the boot of miracles, with 1.1 million changes of clothing and wigs to help us blend in.

We make our way to the hotel lobby and decide there are two areas in which we can sit. If we stay in them, our target will have to pass us before leaving the building, because there's no other possible way out. Best thing is for me to take one area and for Steph to take the other.

Steph takes the lobby and I go and fetch the car to park it outside, just in case they get in a taxi from the hotel. The only problem is there's no legal parking outside the hotel, so I abandon it on double yellows and hope they don't have too many parking wardens in Brighton. I take my place in reception near the front door. My BlackBerry Messenger buzzes.

STEPHERS: 'They're on their way, for BREAKFAST! I'm staaaaarrrrrrvvvvviiiinnnngggg!!!!!!!'

I look up, and all ten of them are passing me and heading into the restaurant. Our target is trailing behind with one other friend. Steph is also not far behind. She very firmly points her finger in the direction of food, and gestures for me to follow. I'm not going to lie, I don't need much persuasion.

We take a seat behind a column where we can't be seen by them. We both order a full English, because on this job you never know when or where your next meal is coming from. Fifteen minutes later and our breakfasts are in front of us, but within five minutes of their arrival our target is on the move.

'Oh shit,' Steph says, mouth half-full of bacon, sausage and tomato sauce. She slams her knife and fork on the table and stands up. I say nothing, but leave my wonderful breakfast a quarter of the way through and make my way straight out of the side entrance to avoid any eye contact with the target. I turn back, and see Steph gathering some sausages into a napkin, then she follows the lads.

I'm in the car, the engine is running, and the group are gathered at the front of the hotel. They're waiting for what I can only assume is a taxi. Steph casually crosses the road, opens the door and slides herself into the back seat.

'Think they're waiting for a taxi,' she says.

'Well done, brains.' Sure as anything, a minibus pulls up, they all pile in and off we go.

'Sausage?' Steph asks, holding one out for me.

'Think I'll pass.'

'Your loss.'

The minibus pulls up outside a huge building. There are no signs so we can't tell what it is.

'Hmm, interesting,' Steph remarks. 'It must be fifteen stories high. What do you think it is?'

I tell her I've absolutely no idea, but we're about to find out. Our target is moving inside, and we have no choice but to follow. At this point, if we were in a movie we would probably have some silly theme tune music – as usual I imagine *Benny Hill* music playing in the background as we play cat and mouse. The target walks, we wait, run, watch, wait, run, watch. Hide behind corners, doors or anything we can find. To anyone watching (hopefully no one is) it looks utterly ridiculous – but it's necessary.

This looks like a hotel entrance. The boys keep walking through two double doors, another set and finally another. Before we know it, we're in what looks like a disused factory at the back of the building.

'Go-karting!' Steph remarks, while nodding her head as if she knew all along.

'Girls! Are you here to join us?' a very polite man asks. He's standing behind the desk where all the outfits are. He clearly works here, as he's in fancy overalls.

'Do we really look like the type to be go-karting?' I ask him, raising an eyebrow and leaning on his counter.

Before he can answer I turn round to see our target and his group walking towards us. I look to my left, to my right and there's nowhere for us to run. Steph spins round to overall man. 'Give me two helmets really, really fast!!'

The man sees we're not to be messed with and virtually throws the helmets into our hands. We shove them on our heads super-quick and stand there looking at each other.

'I look like a spoon,' Steph says.

'Me too.'

We walk straight past the target to the other side of the go-karting track. We find ourselves a little seat and stay there for the next two hours, watching the target whizz round and round the track. All the time we keep our helmets on our knees, just in case.

The group head for the bar and spend the next three hours there. In total we've now spent six hours in a go-karting centre and that's all we've done.

Once again they head outside and dive into the minibus, which has been waiting all this time. We follow them back into the town, and they do very little. In fact, all they do is go back to the hotel, get changed and head for the hotel bar.

We sit outside in the restaurant. It has a floor-to-ceiling glass window, so we can see everything they're doing and they have absolutely no idea. Another two hours pass, and when I check I realise the car has picked up not one but two parking tickets. Hazard of the job, I'm afraid, but a major pain either way! Must remember to start charging for at least two parking tickets per case in future.

Just as Steph is about to doze off, they look as if they're making a move. Our client has picked up his pint and is drinking the rest down really fast. I know this sign and so I rush for the door.

I'm parked on the main road when they emerge from the hotel entrance, speaking on the phone to Steph, who's hanging back in one of the hallways.

'They're out of the main entrance. Looks like they're going on foot. Taken a left, and they're going up the alley at the side of the hotel.'

'Oh shit,' she says as she emerges from the front entrance and realises what is up the alleyway at the side of the hotel – a hundred steep steps leading to a walkway into the main part of town. 'See, Rebecca, this is why you need to give us all free membership to a gym. I am NOT fit enough for these steps.'

It's a narrow set of steps, and our client and his gang are halfway up. It's vital Steph gets a move on because if they reach the top and make any sudden movements, we could lose them. Unfortunately I can't help. Someone has to drive to wherever they end up during this little walking mission. After their next stop they might jump in a taxi, and then we'd be snookered. People may think it's common, but it's not always possible to jump into a taxi and shout 'Follow that car!'

Steph has tackled about thirty steps. 'Bitch, I hate you right now.'

'Come on, Steph. You can do it.'

'PATRONISING BLOODY COW.' She's not happy.

The target is now out of sight so she has to hurry. 'GO, Steph!'

'I'm so frigging unfit, this is ridiculous.'

She musters all her energy and watching from the bottom of the steps I see her attack the situation as if it's an army assault course.

'That's it, not far to go,' I encourage.

Steph looks down at me and wags her finger. 'If you don't shut the hell up I'm going to come back down them steps, because it will be a lot easier than carrying on, and I'm going to ram your phone down your neck. Piss off and try to find where this arsehole alleyway leads.'

'OK, but just so you know all that energy you used ranting at me could have been used a lot more productively in getting up the steps.'

She ignores me and hangs up. Not going to lie – very pleased it's her and not me.

I drive past the hotel and up the one-way system. I always find one-way systems a pain. Most certainly the way you want to go is the wrong one. You can look round and see where you want to be, but no, the system makes you go the long way round, then it takes twenty minutes to navigate your way back to where you started. If it's a town you don't actually know, then God help you.

Thankfully, this time it's not too difficult. The only problem is that Steph is going to end up in a pedestrian-only zone. There's nothing I can do to help her. She's on her own now.

Ten minutes later, the phone rings.

'Are you on them?' I ask.

'Yes.'

'Where are you?'

'I have no sodding idea.'

'Great. What's around?'

'Pubs.'

'Come on, throw me a bone. What else?'

'More pubs.'

'OK, never mind. I'll trace you now.' I hang up on her. This problem occurs quite a lot when we're in towns we've never seen before. So we installed trackers onto all our phones, which solves the problem instantly. Just wish we could use them on our clients!

I fire up the laptop and trace the exact pub she's in. It takes me all of six minutes to get there. When I arrive, Steph is behind a pot plant, and she's bouncing from one foot to the other.

'What's wrong with you?' I ask.

'I need a peeeeeeee.' One day I'm going to invent a toilet device for the private investigation industry. I keep meaning to get round to it. The target is sitting at a table outside another pub with two of his buddies.

'Come on, let's go in.' We both walk casually into the pub, just out of sight of the target. Once through the door, Steph bolts for the toilet. I take a seat just back from the front window. The pub interior is dark so he can't see me. I pull out the smallest video camera we have and take some footage. Steph arrives back from the toilet looking very cheery.

'Better?' I ask.

'Much, thank you!'

Next we know, five men sit at our table. Considering the pub is packed full of people that's not too unusual. The fact they are dressed as the men from Village People's 'Y.M.C.A.' video is a bit different.

'Can we join you?'

'Course you can, loves.' Anything that gives us a cover is a good thing, although there is quite a fine line between a cover and making us stand out.

Three hours later. Our client is still in the same pub, but has moved inside. The Y.M.C.A. crew are our new best friends. They tell us they're from Glasgow, on a stag do, but the stag has pulled some ugly woman and they've lost him. (Note to self: must send his soon-to-be wife our card!) The builder type loves his mum very much, all but one of them is taken, they all hate Brighton, their favourite drink is Guinness, they wish they'd gone to Ireland, they're staying at a hostel, they hate the hostel, they want to gatecrash our hotel (part of me is worried they will) … I'm quite relieved to see our target begin to move before they start sharing anything more intimate. I nudge Steph.

'Lads, it's been a blast,' she tells them, as we stand to leave.

'Wait, where are you going?' the copper type (Tony) asks us.

'Don't know yet.' Steph is downing her drink.

'Well in that case, we're coming with youuuuu,' they say, all merry and pleased with themselves.

'Greaaaaat.'

It's a long trek for us to follow the target to his next location … right next door!

More hours go by. It's now dark. We've done nothing but sit and watch him drink.

Builder type is getting emotional and slurring his words as he confides in me: 'My mum was such an angel when my dad died. She was remarkable, but I didn't cope very well. It was so sad, he was my best friend, but Mum's doing a really good job of taking his place.'

They've bought us four rounds of shots, none of which I've drunk: one I threw in a plant behind me when they simply couldn't comprehend the excuse 'I AM DRIVING'. Steph drank two of them, and the other one is still on the table in front of me.

The groom has turned up again, and tells us all about what he's been up to with dirty bird. They went back to the hostel – how classy. He starts to confide in Steph about his up-and-coming marriage, saying he's not totally sure it's the right idea. He feels he's been railroaded into it.

They keep asking what we do for a living, and we keep dodging the question.

Target begins to move again … This time when we stand up to leave and they ask where we're going, Steph pulls one of our flyers from her handbag.

'So you want to know what we do? Here you go.' And she puts it down on the table.

Their faces are a picture. 'Oh my God,' one says.

'Have you been investigating me?' The groom is alarmed.

'No, love. If we were investigating you, you wouldn't have seen us – and you're just not that lucky.' Steph walks out.

'Although, I would keep the gory details of what you get up to behind your fiancé's back to yourself,' I add. 'We haven't been investigating you, but you never know when some random lady you start chatting to might be.' I give my biggest smile, and pinch the cheek of his now very shocked face.

Potentially Steph just pulled a risky stunt, but it was hilarious. I should have been furious, and usually I would be. However I think that groom needed teaching a lesson, and we were in no immediate danger. Steph promises she won't do it again, though.

We spend the next few hours following the target from pub, to pub, to pub, to club. They've now been drinking for around sixteen or seventeen hours. How on earth they're still standing, I don't know. We're bored utterly senseless. I'm sure we've broken some European law about working too long without a break. Food is always difficult to come by on jobs. Well, proper food is. We have to grab whatever we can, when we can. Three packets of crisps and a chocolate bar is all I have managed at this point. The party we're following seem to have no intention of eating proper food! I hate days like this. I get an awful taste in my mouth when I've eaten nothing but rubbish. Simply nothing we can do about it though.

At 5am the target is on the outdoor terrace of a nightclub. He can't even see past the end of his nose, he's so drunk. I fetch the car and pull up on double yellow lines outside the pub. Steph gets in and watches him through binoculars. The door staff watch us like hawks. The car we're using is rather obvious – a top-of-the-range sports car with blacked-out windows. I get stick for using it, but the problem is that if we have an unknown entity on our hands, we might need a high-speed, high-powered car. It often raises eyebrows, but the risk is outweighed, in my opinion.

The bouncers are talking to the police and pointing at us. Amazing. Can't drive off or it would look really suspicious and they'd just put out a call to stop us at the next opportunity.

'Evening, ladies.' A copper has made his way over to us.

'Hellooooo officer,' Steph replies flirtatiously. I glare at her. Not the right time for that.

'How come you've been here so long, and why are you on double yellow lines?' he asks, quite reasonably.

'I can tell you if you promise not to tell anyone,' I say, hoping this will go down well.

'Depends on what you're going to tell me.'

I pull out our flyers and a business card.

'Private investigators?' He seems to find it amusing.

'Caught us red-handed, I'm afraid. Our client is over there.' I point at the beer garden.

'Blimey. What've they done?' he asks.

'Suspected of being unfaithful to his wife,' I tell him, deadly serious.

'Has he done anything?'

'Not a thing, and we've been on him for seventeen hours!' I complain, looking for sympathy.

'No way. So if I tell you to move now, you might risk the whole job?'

'Something like that,' I tell him. Steph is batting her eyelids.

'Well then, I can't jeopardise your job, can I? Just try not to park on double yellows. If a traffic warden comes along, I can't save you ladies.'

RELIEF!

'Aw, thank you, officer. You're very kind,' Steph says.

'Can I keep the card?' he asks.

'Of course you can.' He bids us goodnight and goes back over to the bouncers. He must tell them about us because they all look over and burst out laughing, giving us the thumbs up.

One hour later … we're still there. Not too long ago there was a famous advert on TV for a car company. The car in question was parked on a driveway, and the young kid of the family was dressed as Darth Vader from *Star Wars*. The kid jumped in front of the car and pointed at its headlights at the same moment that the father, who was standing in the doorway, clicked to unlock the car, and the headlights came on. The kid jumped back astounded, as if it was real magic at work! … So there we are, sitting outside this beer garden when next thing we know, a grown man jumps in front of the car dressed as Darth Vader and points at our headlights. I flash them on and off. He jumps back and everyone standing in the beer garden applauds. NOT the kind of attention we need to attract, but it was amusing.

Those two little incidents were the only vaguely amusing events of hours and hours of very boring surveillance. Thankfully, not long after that our target emerges between the bouncers, staggering. He's on his own, swaying and stumbling down the street. We're surprised he's upright after so many hours of alcohol. I'd probably be hospitalised by now!

Steph gets out of the car. She has changed her clothes in the back seat and donned a black outfit that looks appropriate with flat shoes. Flat shoes always signal it's the end of the night, when we've seriously had enough and just want to go to bed so we can no longer be bothered with how we look. Our make-up hasn't even been reapplied for the past four hours!

The target walks – no, staggers – down a long main road, diverts off to a side street, another side street, is sick over a wall, crosses an alleyway, heads back to the main road, passes the bar he was last in again, heads down another side street … All with Steph in hot pursuit.

'Can we not just stick him in the boot? He's clearly lost!' she texts me.

'No! Follow!' That's all the reply she's getting.

I'm irritated now. It's been forty minutes since he left the bar! Thankfully he eventually finds his way into the hotel, and we are exceptionally relieved. He goes back to his room, and we find ours, collapse and fall asleep within minutes, after a long, boring and irritating day.

The next day is much the same. Nothing whatsoever of any interest. If we'd been following a group of women it would have been a lot more fun! We might actually have got some proper food, visited a spa, gone cupcake making … Oh, the possibilities are endless! Instead, we were landed with this one!

The boys don't head out of the hotel until 12 noon, but we have to be up at 9.30am ready for them. Yes, slightly over three hours' sleep and we have to operate for a whole new, long day. We spend the day going in and out of pubs, once again. Steph debates taking up knitting! Our target stumbles out of his final pub at 3am, and spends forty-five minutes getting lost again.

The next morning we are up at 8am. We know they're going home today, but don't know exactly when. We have to be prepared for all eventualities, as ever!

We've given up trying to be secretive now. We sit on opposite sides of a big table in the hotel reception area, utterly zombiefied, without the energy to move or speak to each other. We are drinking very strong coffee and wearing sunglasses. Thankfully the sun is streaming through the glass windows, so we don't look too ridiculous. This situation has got so bad, we've virtually given up all make-up. We look like shit. I've applied a very thin layer of fake tan, and Touche Éclat. That's it! Since the age of eleven, I've never before left home without a full face of make-up. Well, apart from once when I was thirteen. I went to school with serious stomach pain and a horrific fever. Two days later I was in hospital, having my appendix removed after it nearly burst. That was an extreme circumstance, thus the lack of make-up, and this is similarly extreme. In the past fifty hours, we've slept for just six and a half hours. We are now faced with the possibility of yet another full day's work. What a joke!

'I'm never doing this again without more of us, Bec!' Steph mumbles.

'Agreed.'

We never thought it would be so hardcore. A couple of days out, a couple of nights out – that's all we thought we were getting. But these lot have well and truly hammered the alcohol. They start drinking in the morning and don't stop until they fall into bed.

They all emerge at once. Steph slightly lowers her sunglasses to confirm we're seeing what we think we're seeing then we text each other.

STEPH: 'It's them!'

ME: 'I know, silly.'

STEPH: 'They're sitting next to me.'

ME: 'I can see. I'm not asleep over here. What can you hear?'

STEPH: 'Arsehole bouncers last night. Not letting them in that club.'

ME: 'Because they were slaughtered.'

STEPH: 'One of them had a fight with someone.'

ME: 'Yawn.'

STEPH: 'Sky Sports is on in ten minutes.'

ME: 'Double yawn.'

STEPH: 'David was chatting up some bird.'

ME: 'Oh really? They're all taken.'

STEPH: 'She knocked him back.'

ME: 'This is ridiculous having a conversation via text when we're so close to each other.'

STEPH: 'Agree. Now some football team are coming on telly.'

ME: 'I can't stand watching them watch a whole match.'

STEPH: 'Talking about work now.'

ME: 'I'm going to the car.'

STEPH: 'One of them said he likes your hair.'

ME: 'Idiot.'

STEPH: 'They're going! Airport!'

ME: 'Car! Now!'

We both get in the car, and sit and wait. They emerge with bags, and one of them, a small chunky dude, comes over.

'Lovely ladies! Are you our taxi?'

'No, sorry, we're not.'

'But can you take me and my friend anyway? You'd be the prettiest taxi drivers we've ever had in our whole lives.'

'Awww. Sorry. We're picking up a friend,' I tell him with a smile.

He thanks us and clears off. Their minibus arrives and we follow them to the airport. Job over.

★   ★   ★

Back home we ponder the situation. Our client was convinced her husband would be unfaithful, and I suppose we were too. It's that same age-old thing. People worry that infidelities happen on a night out, and stag events are a particular worry. They've been built up to be the 'last night of freedom'. In theory, it means that anything goes, and I expect quite a few men stray on their stag nights. The truth of the matter is, though, that infidelities rarely happen on boys' nights out because of the amount of alcohol consumed. One-night stands are probably quite rare, and anyway the biggest problem is when relationships form and it becomes an affair.

These men had days away from anyone they knew and they could have thought, as rock stars do, 'What goes on tour, stays on tour.' If anything had happened, they would cover for each other. They had a free pass.

Yet they did absolutely nothing except drink and drink and drink some more. Fish would have died of drowning if they'd drunk as much as these men. They talked about nothing of any interest, and didn't even acknowledge the existence of the opposite sex!

Do we women generally just give men a bad rap? Do we consider them guilty before they've been proved innocent? I think so in this case. I know I certainly won't look at stag parties in the same way again. It was just a group of men, out to have a good time. That being said – someone needs to give them a talking to about alcohol abuse!!

THE ONE THAT
BREAKS US?

———

'Mooorning, Bec!' There's a super-cheery voice at the end of
my phone. Considering it's Monday morning, 7am, I'm not
thrilled. This person clearly knows me because they used my
name. 'Are you asleep?' Cheery Voice asks.

'Yes,' I grump.

'No surprise there, then.' Cheery Voice must know me
well. Hmm.

'My mum's friend needs some help, and I think you may
be the lady for the job.' Slowly the fog begins to lift and
I realise who the voice is. It's Toni – she's worked with us
a couple of times and has been a friend for a few years.
Lovely girl.

'Sorry, love. Didn't recognise you for a second. You know
me and my sleep!'

'Of course I do, don't worry! Anyway … Mum's friend.'

'Yes, sorry, go on. Tell me what the problem is.'

'Well, you may not believe it. It's a bit strange.'

'Honestly, I don't think I can be surprised by anything any
more!' I tell her.

'Mum's friend is a man, and he married a lady from Brazil.
One thing and another, she's come over here and lived with

him for the last couple of years, and now she's done a runner … With their pet! He wants to find her.'

'That's not that strange!' I tell her, laughing, although I don't think I should be laughing.

'Do you want me to send you his email address?' Toni asks.

'Go on then, fire it over and I'll see what he wants.' We end the conversation, and I'm still chuckling to myself. The gentleman in question is apparently called Phillip. I send him an email and roll back over to sleep. When I finally, properly, wake – around 11am – I do wonder if my earlier conversation had all been part of a dream. I'm wearing my Tinkerbell nightie, because Paris loves it. I rub my eyes and walk over to the computer, bumping into things on my way. The sound of me thudding into my chair makes me wonder if I need to diet. I honestly do make the noise of a baby elephant when sitting down. That, or I'm a clumsy sod. I shrug it off as my email is making lots of trumping sounds.

I've had an email back from Phillip, so it definitely wasn't a dream. I read it and draw the conclusion that he's shy and a little introverted. I feel rather sorry for him. He's poured his heart out about his background, the story of his relationship and why he's in the position he's in. He's told me his life story, but everything he writes has an air of nervousness and insecurity about it. It seems he's potentially a very complex character, with a very complex case. Or perhaps he's simply heartbroken, and can't hide it?

We exchange more emails over the course of the next couple of days, and he wants to meet us. Usually I don't like to meet clients face to face for security reasons, but he seems harmless. And the most important thing is that he knows one of our ladies. We'll be safe with this guy, I'm sure. So I agree.

Three days later, I'm outside Steph's house.

'Morning, bird,' she says, climbing into the car with three handbags, two cardigans, three dresses, one pair of leggings, two tops, a bottle of nail varnish and a make-up bag in hand.

'What the hell are you doing?' I ask, puzzled by the sheer amount of stuff she's now throwing over into the back seat.

'Why am I here again?' she asks.

'Er, because we're going to see that client whose Brazilian wife left him.'

'Oooooooh. Right.'

'What did you think you were doing?'

'Well, to be honest, I didn't know. You rang, I was drunk. I just knew when I woke up this morning that my memo said 'REBECCA 11AM WORK!' So I got out of bed and prepared for every eventuality. Never know what I'm doing, or what I'll need, with you!' In all fairness to Steph, she's not a raging alcoholic – I did call her at 10pm on a Saturday evening.

'As much as you're totally crackers, I'm slightly impressed with the preparation.' I personally don't need it. The boot of the car *is* Narnia after all.

'Where are we going now?' she asks.

'We're off to get Jess,' I tell her.

'Then we're meeting Mr Brazil?'

'Yes.'

'Well, that's different. Why are we seeing him?' Steph is curious.

'He's harmless, he knows Toni and he really wants to meet us and talk us through it. To be fair, the case sounds really damn complicated, so I need you all to pay loads of attention and take notes. I'm bound to forget everything!'

We get Jess and head over to the Tree-House. The Tree-House is our wonderful new office, based on a country-park estate. It's a real tree house made out of wood, with wooden steps up to it and we rent it to use whenever we have to meet anyone. It's very homely. There's even a Starbucks on site, which gets a lot of business from us, as you can imagine.

Just as we've sat down with our skinny lattes and set up our notes and computers, there's a timid knock on the door.

'Come in!' Jess shouts.

'Hello.' A very slim gentleman walks in, as nervously as I'd expected. He has short dark hair, grey glassy eyes and is medium height. I stand to greet him.

'Hi,' I say, giving my best, cheery 'welcome' smile and holding out my hand. 'You're Phillip?'

'I am. Are you Rebecca?'

'I sure am. This is Stephanie and this is Jess,' I say, pointing at them. Steph is tucking into her latte, and Jess is smiling and waving with one hand while propping up her chin with the other. 'Nice to meet you at last. Can I get you a drink or some water?' I'm trying my hardest to make him feel at ease.

'Er, yes please. I'll, er, have a coffee?' He's even nervous asking for a coffee.

'I'll get it,' Steph walks over to the kettle. She isn't the best at brew-making, but she'd rather do that than walk all the way back to Starbucks. If she drops it in his lap and scalds him for life, he's not going to be very at ease then!

'So, your wife. She sounds like a character!' I'm trying to lighten the mood.

'She certainly is that.' He broke into a smile! Miracle.

'Do you want to start from the beginning? I know it's not easy but, honestly, you can tell us anything. We've heard almost everything before.'

'That's true,' Jess chirps, rolling her eyes.

'No problem. Well, I met her five years ago, on holiday. We then chatted for over a year through online chat services, and she seemed very lovely.'

Don't they all?

'One thing and another, I went over to Brazil for a few months at a time, before we eventually decided we'd get married.'

'OK, and where did the marriage take place? Here or Brazil?' Jess asks him, taking notes. We all take notes at meetings in case we forget anything.

'No, it was actually on holiday in Las Vegas.'

'Did you come over here and do the ceremony again?' I wonder if the type of ceremony they had is even legal here.

'No, just that one.' We both nod, and he continues as Steph brings his coffee, drips rolling down the sides. Come on Steph, be strong: I will her with all my power not to spill it in his lap.

'There. Any sugar?' she asks, placing it safely on the table. Phew.

'No, that's fine, thank you.' Relief. Focus back on Phillip.

'We didn't stay long in Brazil. It was proving difficult for me to find work, and I didn't really want to stay there, so we moved here.'

'Was that your choice or hers?' Steph asks. You can tell that we're all on his side and think she's the devil that's conned him. Oh dear, a judgemental streak is creeping back into us again!

'It was mine. She didn't want to leave her family, specifically her mum, behind. She was very close to them.'

'What's your wife called?' I ask.

'Lais.' I get him to spell it for us.

'OK, so you came here and what happened then?'

'Well, it was OK. I didn't realise there was a problem, but I now think she planned it all along. We came here and she struggled to fit in. She missed her mum a lot, and made no friends. I felt really bad for her. I wanted her to be happy and to fit in. But it was difficult. Eventually she made some friends, though – one was called Bisi.'

'How did she meet Bisi?' Steph asks.

'I met her, actually.' Bless him, Phillip seems proud of this. 'I met her in Tesco, when I was doing my weekly shop.'

'You met her in Tesco?' Jess repeats.

'Tesco!' he says.

'How did that happen?'

'She was at the fish counter when I was buying sardines.'

Steph throws me a sidelong glance that I notice out of the corner of my eye. We're already suspicious of Bisi.

'She was talking to the lady behind the counter, and I could hear the twang in her accent. I knew she sounded Brazilian. So I asked her, and she said I was right. I told her my wife was struggling to fit in here as she had no friends and that she needed to make some. I asked her to come for tea one night, and she accepted.'

I can't imagine that if anyone came over to me in a supermarket and asked me for tea to meet his wife, I would say yes. Very bizarre. Or is this a kind and lovely thing to do for the woman he loves? I'm not sure.

'Then what happened?' Jess asks.

'They got on really well. We all did. And then she introduced Lais to her community group, who were all from Brazil.

They met once a month. It really helped her. Bisi's still a good friend of mine now. She still tells me what Lais is up to. Last time I spoke to her she told me she was in London with a man she met online and was quite happy, and not coming back.'

'Oh, really? Would you say she's your friend or Lais's now?' I ask him.

'Both. We both still talk to her, and I'm going to see her after I leave here, in fact.'

This is interesting. This Bisi seems key to the problem.

'So she knows exactly where your wife is, I assume?'

'Oh yes, she knows where she is.' He seems to be clamming up a bit, talking about it.

'But?' I ask.

'I don't like to put her in an awkward position. I think it wouldn't be right to ask her too many questions.'

He has a direct link to his wife, he wants to find out where his wife is, but yet he won't ask Bisi 'too many questions'. This is very strange. It doesn't add up. But I'm going to have to stop probing on this point, or he'll go back into his shell. Now, however, I definitely feel he's coming out a bit.

'Did she work?' I ask.

'She did, yes, as a care worker. In a home for the deranged.'

I glance over at Steph, who's looking very confused. I wonder what the other two ladies are thinking. I mean, this is getting odder and odder.

'Was she always a care worker?'

'No, back home she was a banker. She had a really good job – very intelligent lady. Coming over here, though, no one recognised her qualifications and she couldn't get work. Her English isn't the best either. It's OK, but not the best.'

'Blimey! Did she like looking after people?'

'Not much, but she liked getting out of the house. Probably to get away from me.'

You can tell he's serious, and that's rather sad. I glance up from my notes to see him gazing at the floor. Poor man.

'Did she make any friends at work? Anyone you can tell us about?' I ask, trying to bring the conversation back to practicalities.

'Not really. She kept herself to herself, but her boss was lovely. I've spoken to her since, and she's very nice. Although she does say the same thing – that Lais was very quiet and just came in to do her job.'

Now, I think, there's something to check. People spend so much time at work there's not a chance no one knows anything about her. I need to speak to the boss.

'When did it all go wrong, then?' Jess asks.

'She'd always been very depressed, and I knew things weren't good. I think she calculated it all, though. You have to be in this country for a certain amount of time before you can claim any kind of benefits, and she'd been here just over one week after that point. I went to work in the morning as usual, spoke to her during the day, as usual. I came home, and she'd gone. Everything she had went with her, including £2,000 I had in cash for a holiday we were planning back in Brazil, and our pet ferret.'

I try very hard to keep a straight face.

'Why do you think she left?'

'Because she was unhappy. And I think she'd met someone else on the Internet. The one Bisi told me about. Lais was constantly glued to her computer – day and night – when she was in. Chatting away to lots of people.'

Jess and Steph are looking sympathetic, but I can tell they find it bizarre as well.

'Blimey. Not a great story, is it?' I genuinely feel sorry for him. 'So, I assume you want to find her and the man she's with? The money? Do you want to get it back, or call the police about it?'

'Oh no, no, I'm not bothered about the money. Or about her. I just want the ferret back!'

Steph sprays out some of her latte, then tries to stifle her amusement with a pretend coughing fit.

'Sorry, the ferret? You just want to find the ferret?' Jess and I are equally as bemused, but trying desperately not to laugh.

'Yes, just the ferret. She can do what she wants, with whom she wants. I want the ferret. I know it's strange, but I want it back.'

I stare down at my notes, furiously scribbling nonsense in order to stop myself from laughing.

'I'm sorry, you have to admit that it's a little funny,' Steph tells him.

She's going with the theory that addressing the problem makes it OK. I, too, think that's best, and he seems to be seeing the funny side with us.

'I know. It's not very normal, is it? It's just it had a near-death experience once – it got out of its cage and found its way into the washing machine. It could have very nearly ended its little life, so I do feel very protective over it.'

The mood goes back to depressing.

'So it's a miracle ferret, then,' says Jess.

'You could say that. Lais hated that ferret, though, and I loved it. I don't understand why she took it.'

'That poor ferret.' In the space of two minutes, Steph has gone from laughing to nearly bursting into tears! I glance at her then back at Phillip.

'What was the ferret called?' I ask him.

'Woofels was what she called it.'

'Woofels? What was it called before she called it Woofels?'

'Furby,' he says.

'Why did she change its name?' Wondering if I'm missing something.

'Well, really she wanted a dog, but I refused to get any more pets while Furby was alive.'

I actually can't believe we're having this conversation like serious adults. People often joke with us that we're like female Sherlock Holmeses (until they spend ten minutes with us and realise how nuts we are), but I don't think anyone ever compared us to Ace Ventura!

'How long is it since your wife left?'

'About six weeks. I've been trying to decide what to do since then, and now you're my last resort'.

I take a deep breath. 'Right, OK, we'll do everything we can to find the ferret, then,' I tell him, trying to wind this conversation up pretty quickly. We take a few more details from him, about what the ferret looks like, this Bisi character and where Lais worked. We wave him on his way down the steps of the Tree-House, and resume our seats.

'I feel I've just done twenty rounds with Mike Tyson!' Jess says, breathing a huge sigh of relief.

'Just let me get this clear. Wife comes over from foreign country, basically plans to rip him off. Uses him for a visa, and to get on benefits. Clears off when she meets someone else, takes husband's money … And all he wants is his ferret back?' Steph says, confused and dazed.

'That is totally correct. How absolutely random! How do we find a ferret?' I lean back in the seat.

'I actually don't know because my brain is now officially mashed!' Jess says. I stare out of the window. The sun is shining outside, and I can't face another minute of sitting in this Tree-House.

'Right,' I say, getting up from my chair. 'We're going to her workplace to talk to the boss.'

'Is it too early for alcohol?' Jess asks, gathering up her notes.

'Yes, Jess, it is. No drinking on the job!'

We all climb down the steps from the Tree-House and get into the car. I've given Phillip a task. I've asked him to see if Bisi will agree to have a conversation with me because I think she is the key to solving this situation (and finding the ferret). I reassured him that the whole reason our agency does so well is because we're totally unthreatening. We're not your average private investigators, steaming into a situation in a ruthless manner. We really do care – we even care about this ferret. We may find it slightly amusing, mainly because the situation is outright bizarre – but we care! He said he would come back to me later in the day and let me know if Bisi will talk to me.

The home where Lais worked is a long way from a main road, apparently to stop patients escaping, but it's not too far from the Tree-House. We drive over two miles down what is effectively a dirt track. By the time we reach the home, we could be on any moor in the country. It's totally wild, and very eerie.

'Are you pair coming in?' I ask Steph and Jess, getting out of the car.

'Are we hell!' Steph exclaims from the back seat, where she is munching an apple. 'You're the master at this shit. Knock yourself out.'

I don't bother to respond. Instead I smooth down my suit jacket and walk across the gravel driveway in my heels. That's no easy task. I sink and slightly lose my balance before finally making it to the stone paving at the front entrance. Just as I get there, some relatives are emerging after a visit. They hold the door for me and I walk in. Easy.

There's no reception as such; I walk directly into what seems to be a large lounge. Lots of reclining chairs around, with people sat in them. No one saying very much, a couple of people staring blankly at a TV. One lady is knitting in a corner while another gentleman is rocking back and forth in his chair. I realise I'm hovering, looking aimless. I refocus, and try to find someone in authority.

As I walk towards the back of the lounge I hear a noise from behind me. It's a babble. Someone not making sense, or talking in a foreign language. I turn around and see a man who must be about seventy. He's very thin, with white hair, and wearing a typical granddad cardigan – cream, heavy-knit with brown buttons. He's shuffling along, making a drumming movement with his hands: 'Ha buh mum bah. Ta vu sha. Hob ob fob fob.' I think it's best to ignore him and keep trying to find someone official but he starts following me.

I walk through to what looks like a dining room. Three residents are eating in silence. My new friend is bumbling behind me still. I stand out like a sore thumb, but no one is paying any attention. 'Um bum ah ah bah. Far na nar.' No one in here.

I go through a door into another lounge. This place is like a rabbit warren. No one is here at all. Bumbling is still following. Next door leads to a corridor. Nothing. I turn around and go back to the first lounge. Still no one in authority.

I can't believe this. Go back to dining room. FOUND someone! Happy days! Bumbling is *still* following.

'Hi, is it possible to speak to the owners, please?' I ask the
girl, who's no older than twenty.

'Sure, do you want to book someone in?' It takes all my
effort not to say 'Myself' but … 'No, it's about a former
employee,' I tell her. Bumbling has sat down. 'HA bo bo ha
mum ta …'

'No problem, I'll go and get Jenny.' She walks off, leaving
me with Bumbling: 'Oo oo way ka kam oo ta.'

I'm on my own with him for about ten minutes before
Jenny, the owner, turns up. She seems nice (big smiles). Rather
scruffy-looking, though.

'Hi! I'm Jenny!' she says, offering her hand, which
I shake.

'Hi Jenny. I've got a bit of a strange request.' I thought she
would lead me to an office or something, but no. We stand
there and talk on the spot, with Bumbling behind me. He
seems to be getting louder so it's very hard to focus. 'I'm a
private investigator and I'm actually trying to find a missing
ferret.' I wonder if 'missing' is the appropriate term, or if
I should have said 'stolen'?

'Oh, right,' she says, looking as confused as I was when
I first heard this story.

'I know it's a bit strange, but it's been taken by a former
employee of yours. A Brazilian lady, Lais.' I can tell from her
face she recognises the name.

'Yes, I know Lais.'

The next thing I know, Bumbling has got out of his seat
and is standing two inches away bumbling *in my face*. Very
loudly. 'Bum tan tum al la la is oh my.'

'Lais left us about a month ago now.' Is she really just going to continue this conversation as if he's not here? 'She was very quiet, didn't say much to anyone.' Yes, clearly Bumbling is not bothering her. He's still two inches from my face, and I'm even having to strain to see Jenny. This is downright weird. 'Actually, the person who knew her best was Serena, but she's not here today.'

'LAAAAAAAA HAAAAAAA LAAAAAAAA ...' Now he's almost singing.

'I can get her to call you, if you want? I didn't know her at all but she used to chat to Serena,' Jenny tells me.

'That's excellent. Can I leave you my number?' Thankfully, she agrees and walks towards the window where there's a pad and paper. It's a relief to be able to move from the spot I've been rooted to throughout this conversation where a man who's clearly not all there is bumbling loudly in my face. As much as I feel hugely out of my comfort zone, I think the bumbling man is very sad. It must be awful not being able to communicate. Crikey, I wasn't banking on this when I took on the job.

I thank Jenny for her time and make my way to the exit. Bumbling is still following me, and I don't know what to do. Fortunately a member of staff comes rushing after us to catch him. They pull him back, as if they think he will try to break free as soon as I open the door. A very disturbing sight – and situation, for that matter. I shut the entrance door, making sure it's secure. Then I run – well, as fast as my heels can take me – across the gravel, stumbling and sinking at a much quicker pace than I entered. I throw myself into the car, shut the doors and lock them.

'What the hell just happened to you?' Jess turns to me.

'Don't even ask!'

I drive as fast as I possibly can down the driveway and back to the main road. If I ever have a problem, that is one 'home' I never want to be resident in!

★   ★   ★

We're sat in the local pub – well, they'd probably call it a 'wine bar' or a 'gastro-pub'. It's one of those places where you go to feel a bit posh but no one really is 'posh'. They all pretend to be millionaires, and they drive Bentleys but live in terraced houses. None of the customers were born and bred in our village either – they all flock here because it's the 'latest' place to be seen. Point being, I'm sat with Steph and Jess over a working lunch. We're attempting to digest 'special fries' – which are a bit like classic thin-cut French fries but with Parmesan on top – and home-made burgers. Utterly amazing.

We expected it to provide the fuel for a new attack on our investigation about a missing ferret. Actually we're all about to be sick from over-indulgence, and silently miserable because we don't have a flaming clue what to do.

'Phillip rang me yesterday,' I announce. 'Not great news. He won't let us speak to Bisi. He says it will put her in a difficult position. Personally, I'm convinced she knows where his wife is and is leading him a merry dance. The only bit of interesting information is that he says Lais is in a village outside Edinburgh, apparently. She's withdrawn some money from a cashpoint, using her debit card. The account had £10 in, and that's exactly what she's withdrawn. Lais knows that Phillip has access to her online banking, though.'

'Strange he won't let us talk to Bisi. He was really defensive,' Steph says.

'Yes, I agree, but I think the money thing is a red herring,' I say to the girls.

'Why?' Jess asks, trying to stifle a burp.

'Nice, Jess!' She mumbles an apology. 'Because it's too obvious. This woman has plotted her getaway for months – she's not as stupid as she makes out. She used to be a banker. She has some brains.'

'Fair point,' Steph nods in agreement. 'I think she's done it on purpose. Taken a little break to the Scottish place, and withdrawn some money from a cashpoint to make it look like she's there. Maybe she's calculating that if Phillip believes she is outside Edinburgh somewhere, he won't bother to look for her. Then she's getting Bisi to feed information back to him, like being in London when she's not. Just so he's really confused.'

'I agree,' says Jess, coming back to life. 'According to Serena, her friend at the home, the man she was getting friendly with online, the one she's suspected to have run off with, is from Manchester. I've found a profile of him online. I can't find much else but I do know he has children. Basically on our doorstep. It's unlikely he'd just leave them for London. If she is on our doorstep, she knows someone could quite easily find her. So she's trying to throw us – and him – off the scent.' She sits back in her chair, like she's just solved the world's greatest murder case. Jess makes me smile!

'Phillip emailed me yesterday and said apparently she went back to Brazil a month ago for two weeks, to see her family. I'm not entirely sure how he knows this, or if it's true. If it is, though, the chances are she put the ferret in whatever the ferret version of a kennel or cattery is,' I muse.

'I don't think she's got the money for a kennel or cattery.' Steph has a valid point.

I never thought I'd say this, but we're well on the path to being defeated. Is this the case that could break us? Our first official total failure? Over a ferret?

Now we're clutching at straws. We ring the RSPCA but no one has surrendered a ferret. Next we call Phillip and ask again about talking to Bisi, but he still won't put us in touch, even though she is now officially our only lead.

And then – Phillip stops returning our calls. He disappears off the radar. In some ways it's a relief because we're totally baffled by the case and have totally failed to find the Brazilian wife and the ferret.

'What do you reckon happened?' Jess asks us when we're sitting around in the Tree-House doing a post-mortem. 'I feel as though we haven't been told the whole story here so we were never going to be able to solve the case. I've been wondering why his wife would have run off with the ferret, and the only solution I can come up with is that she was fond of it or even thought of it as hers in some way.'

'Or she wanted to hurt him and thought that was a way of getting at him,' Steph suggested.

'Do you think it was really the ferret he wanted to find?' I chip in. 'Or was that an excuse? Maybe he was secretly hoping that if we found his wife, he would be able to persuade her to go back with him? I'm not sure that would ever have happened, though. She took elaborate precautions to make sure he didn't find her.'

'If only we had been allowed to talk to Bisi directly. I'm sure you'd have been able to get the whole story out of her, Rebecca,' Jess tells me.

'Either that or we could have put her under surveillance to see if she led us to the wife …'

'Hey! Maybe the reason Phillip has stopped contacting us is because his wife has come back now and he doesn't want her to know he hired private investigators to find her,' Steph suggests, ever the optimist.

But once Phillip stopped calling, we had to call it a day on this one. We hate to admit defeat, but life isn't always neat and tidy, like the ending of an episode of *Murder, She Wrote*. In real life, there are cases that never do get solved, for whatever reason, and we just had to chalk up this case as one of them.

MR PERFECT

Paris and Ben hit it off from the get go. They first meet at my parents' house. It is also the first day he meets Mum and Dad, and he isn't fazed at all. I think most men would be scared to death of so many important introductions in one day, but no. He is really excited and has been looking forward to it for weeks.

He walks through the front door into the long hallway. I am there to greet him, and hanging around behind me in the entrance to the kitchen is Paris. She is trying to secretly look while acting like she doesn't care.

Ben walks down the hallway and kneels down to her level.

'Hi,' he says. 'I'm Ben. Are you Paris?' She beams a smile back at him and nods.

'Hi, Ben!' The little lady is such a pushover. Ten seconds ago she was portraying cold iceberg territory, and within no time she's warmed up and all the ice has melted! 'Mummy says you like cartoons.'

'I do!' he tells her. 'A lot! Do you have any?'

'Oh yes! I've got *Peppa Pig* and *Fifi*, and *In the Night Garden* is on now!'

'I really like *In the Night Garden*. Can I watch it with you?' he asks. She's so excited to find someone who likes her programmes, I think it's possible she may burst! She nods like a miniature loony tune and takes him by the hand to the living room.

When Mum and Dad come through to say the first hellos, they find Ben firmly planted on the sofa next to Paris, and God help him if he tries to move.

The parents quickly approve and go back to making the Sunday dinner.

'So you're Mummy's new friend?' I hear Paris asking.

'I am, yes. Is that OK with you?'

'Only if you watch more cartoons with me.'

Bossy little madam, I'm smiling to myself. She seems very content in his presence. When I go to get them for dinner, they are already new best friends. Paris gobbles down her dinner so quickly I'm sure she'll be sick, then dashes off to get a selection of toys to bring back to the table to show Ben! I have to tell her to take them to the lounge and that Ben will be in shortly to see her, but she needs to let him finish his dinner first.

The parents don't ask too many probing questions, and everyone gets along just fine. It's actually impossible to not get along with Ben. He knows how to speak to anyone and everyone. Not because he's putting on a front, just because he's so easy-going and laid-back, with a genuine curiosity about other people.

Ben stays until evening. We do all the normal things, like watching television as a family, and Paris shows him every toy she has at my parents' house, as well as her bedroom, the garden, the dogs … and just about anything else that will get his attention. It may only be his first meeting with Mum, Dad and Paris but he instantly fits. It's as if they've all known him forever.

Just after that meeting, Ben takes me back to meet his parents. My own parents' first questions when they were told about Ben revolved around 'Has he been married?' and 'Does he have children?' If I'd answered yes to either question I know they would have panicked. Thankfully I could answer no, and I heard the relief in their voices. It wouldn't have been a deal-breaker, of course, but step-children and ex-partners add complications to any relationship. So I worried that Ben's parents might feel the same way. I mean, who wants their young son to have a relationship with a woman who's not yet thirty but has a child and has been divorced? Why couldn't he find someone without all that baggage?

As it turns out, my worries couldn't have been further from the truth. Ben's parents are delighted to hear I have a little girl and can't wait to meet her. In fact, they're so excited they go racing to the shops to buy toys for her! It's a big worry for any parent how their child will be accepted into a new family.

At first I meet them just with Ben on my own, and for a few occasions after that. They soon became impatient, though, because they are bursting to meet my little bundle of a princess.

Ben's mum invites us all for a sleepover at their house, and I'm touched when I find she has bought a *Peppa Pig* blow-up bed for Paris, who is clearly delighted by it. When I walk into the bedroom at 9pm I find Ben's mum feeding her chocolate ice cream, and watching a film with her. Paris could not be happier. I've not seen her smile so broadly in a long time. I truly feel we've been accepted into Ben's family as if we're biologically theirs.

Paris happily accepts Ben as the new man in our lives and in the autumn, when she first starts going to big school, she begins to call Ben 'Daddy' as if it's the most natural thing in the world. Neither of us questions it or makes an issue of it. If that's how she wants to think of him, that's fine by me because no matter what happens between us, I know he will always take his role in her life 100 per cent seriously.

WHEN SADNESS
HITS NEW LOWS

Steph and I are sitting at the side of a cricket pitch somewhere in the North of England. We're not entirely sure where.

'I think it's highly possible we're in Devon,' Steph tells me, clearly referring to the drive to get here, which felt like it took hours.

'Devon is not where we are, you doughnut.'

'Hmm, maybe you're right.'

We look entirely out of place. I've been attending cricket matches for some time now, thanks to Ben, but I don't think I ever fit in, not really. We're sitting on a bale of hay, and it's uncomfortable. Steph has come along for the day out and keeps fidgeting, manoeuvring herself from one side to the other. Our hair is perfect, and we're both in super-high heels which sank into the grass as we hobbled across. Steph is wearing a short skirt, and I've been slightly more sensible in jeans. Either way, we still don't fit in. Regardless, we enter into the spirit of the game with all our heart. Crowd claps, we clap. Crowd cheers, we cheer.

Within two hours of arriving at the game, the phone is already ringing. It's the out-of-hours service, which is basically just another phone for when it's not usual working hours – not that there are any usual working hours for this job, but at least I know what this means: client! We've moved on this week from detective theme tunes and have a *Sex and the City* ring tone. I thrust the phone into Steph's hands.

'Deal with it,' I tell her.

I'm such a control freak that I don't often let the others take calls but I'm going to have to learn to let go if I want the business to grow bigger. It's good for the others to be in touch with the clients. We don't do it enough but Steph is usually amazing with them.

'Ola, The Lady Detective Agency.' Suddenly I remember that she drank a couple of glasses of wine at lunch. Need to remind myself: don't let her pick up the phone when under the influence. Thankfully her normal composure returns. 'Of course we can … I'm sure we can find that out … I'm sorry to hear that … Oh my … Oh my goodness, that's awful … Really …' The conversation seems to be going on for ever, so I fight my way across the grass to find a bar, and Ben.

Twenty minutes later I peer out of the clubhouse and see Steph still sitting on her hay bale on the phone. She's shaking her head a lot and looks deep in conversation. At one point she even puts her head in her hands. This certainly looks like it could be a very complex and dramatic case.

I hobble back to the hay bales, rosé wine in one hand for Steph and Diet Coke in the other for myself. Someone has to drive. As soon as I reach her, Steph grabs the wine and takes a big gulp, still talking on the phone. My eyes widen in surprise. This sounds a very intense conversation.

'I know … I understand … I can't imagine what you've been through …' The conversation continues for a further forty minutes. In total she's been on the phone for over an hour. When she finally hangs up, she breathes a huge sigh of relief.

'Well. That was interesting.'

'Good interesting or bad interesting?' I ask.

'Good, but sad. Woman needs to get proof of her husband having an affair. She said she knows it's going on, but doesn't know how to prove it.'

'So what was all the drama then?'

'It's just why her husband started the affair that's sad. They had a daughter, and she died.'

'WHAT?' As any parent knows, it's their worst fear in life that their child will die before them. I know that fear. Something deep inside me aches already and I don't even know the details.

'Yep. She was only twelve, and she died of complications after surgery about two years ago.'

'Nooooooo.' I don't know how I'm not actually crying already.

'Her husband has pretty much admitted there's someone else, but won't tell her any more. He says he has then he says he hasn't, and so on.'

'You mean one of those situations where he's admitted it and then changed his mind? Tries to back track and cover it, just in case he decides he wants to save his marriage?'

'Exactly that!' Steph says.

'Ah, yes, I know that type.' Since opening the agency, we've found that human behaviour doesn't always make a lot of sense. We get stuck in patterns and repeat them without stopping to question why. His wife must be in limbo right now. She won't know which version of the story to believe, but he's trying to save his own back.

'And do you want to know the most disturbing part of it all?'

'Go on then.'

'He told her he had the affair because of what happened to their daughter. According to him, she didn't handle the death well enough. She didn't pay him enough attention, and neglected him.'

'He said that?' I'm utterly horrified.

'Apparently so. Disturbing, right?' Steph is obviously deeply affected by the case.

'Wow. That's simply dreadful. The poor woman. How on earth is anyone supposed to handle the death of a child? I'd be traumatised forever. There's no right or wrong way to handle it.'

All of a sudden our cheery happy day at the cricket has turned sour. We both look like depression city sat on our hay. Ben waves over at the pair of us, and we give the most pathetic attempts at a wave back without smiling. He looks puzzled but carries on with the game.

*   *   *

A few days later we find ourselves on a farm. Another place where we don't fit in. We've checked out the location on Google Earth but it can't tell us very much about all the different exits to the property, and we need to find them because we are going to tail the husband. It appears there are five buildings on the site, and at least three exits a car could leave from. Of all the barking daft situations we've found ourselves in, this one certainly takes the biscuit. Steph has a suggestion.

'Let's scale the wall. We've got no option. We need to see where his car is.'

'What do you think we are? Extras in a James Bond film?' I ask.

'No buts, Rebecca. We're doing this.'

I wonder at what point in time I lost my 'boss' position and Steph took over? I watch as she opens the car door and rummages in the boot for wellies. Trailing through fields in heels is not an option, and the grass in these fields doesn't look very normal. In fact it reminds me of a horror story I was part of. The last time I walked through a field like this was when I became intrigued by a derelict building in the middle of it. It was back in the days when I was a property developer, and I would literally do anything to find my next house. It looked so mysterious that I wanted to get closer to look around. I had visions of being captured by squatters and never seeing the light of day again, but instead I was violently attacked by an alien spider. It had clearly been injected with some Spiderman substance to turn it into a mutant. It clung to my jeans and wouldn't let go. Its body was the size of a golf ball with hairs coming out of it. Its eyes were all goggly and its legs were tiny but fat. I screamed my heart out like I was being murdered, but there was no one to save me. I was on my own in the middle of a field, and no one could hear my screams ripping out. I screamed and screamed and screamed even more. I jumped up and down and shook myself violently. Anyone watching would have thought a resident loon had escaped from the local asylum. One way or another I got myself out of the terrifying situation, but I never got close to the building I had wanted to check out and the experience scarred me for life.

Now, standing at the side of a field, with Steph donning fancy wellies and looking to me to follow, I wasn't best pleased. However, we were there for a reason. That reason was our client, the one who'd been told by her husband that she hadn't dealt with the death of their child very well so he just decided to have an affair. The determination in me came back. I put aside my fear of mutant ninja spiders, dived into the boot and found another pair of wellingtons. Today we had to follow him from the farm where he worked to wherever he might end up. Our client suspected it would be into the arms of the woman he said he was/wasn't seeing behind her back. She thought they always met up on the same day each week. The problem was we didn't know which of the three exits out of the farm he would take and if we'd driven our car up the single-track dirt lane we would have aroused suspicion. We couldn't run the risk of picking an exit and hoping for the best, so we had no option but to walk through the five fields that connected them to see where his car was. We were earlier than expected, so there was just enough time to complete a review of the location.

I'm not going to lie. The fear of spiders was still with me as I trampled down the grass, which was over two foot high. Steph, on the other hand, tackled the situation like a pro. A super-girlie girl wearing an outfit that wouldn't look out of place in a Manchester bar at 11pm at night, she was currently accessorising it with wellies and rocking the look. She became my coach and mentor for the next twenty minutes as we went from field to field, reminding me why we were there and urging me that I could do it.

'Bingo!' she shouted. Thankfully we were too far away to be heard by our target, although a mangy-looking dog in the farmyard did look up from his slumbers. Through her binoculars Steph had spotted his car, and determined that it was facing out onto the dirt path, and in the opposite direction from the other two exits we could see. Thankfully they seemed to be blocked off with farm machinery that didn't look as if it would move any time soon. The only way he could go was down the dirt path.

I turned and ran back to my car as fast as my feet would carry me.

Our next stroke of luck came when we reviewed where we would park, ready to follow him. There was a lay-by right near the exit.

'Seriously, we never have this much luck. It's all a bit too easy.'

No job we do has ever been simple. We're both waiting for something to go wrong.

Two hours pass as we wait in the lay-by. We watch one of the latest-release films on the laptop and Steph tries to tempt me with all the 'healthy' treats she's brought along for the mission.

'Cranberry?'

I take a few. 'Yep, they're OK.'

'Almond?'

'No. Hate them.'

'Papaya?'

'Where do you get this random stuff?' I ask her.

'Anywhere and everywhere. Goji berry?'

'Oo, I've heard of these. They're supposed to be really good for you. Like they have super powers or something?'

'Yes, Rebecca, goji berries have super powers. Now do you want one or not?' She shoves the bag under my nose.

'OK, OK, moody.'

I take around five and start to chew them. At first they're OK, but then they turn really sour and vile. I wind down

my window, and it's a good job we're in the middle
of nowhere because I spit them all out. 'They're disgusting!'
I say, screwing up my face, the bitter taste still in my
mouth.

Steph is laughing her head off. 'Yeah, didn't think you'd like
them!'

'You did that on purpose. Like I'm your guinea pig or
something! *So* not funny!' She's still laughing. 'They're like
little pellets of shit!'

There's no water in the car either. We try not to bring
drinks with us on surveillance because of the age-old problem
of drinking lots of fluids and having nowhere to go to the loo!
There's nothing I can do but scrape at my tongue with my
nails to try and get rid of the taste. By this point Steph is
laughing hysterically with tears in her eyes. I give her a dirty
look and out of the corner of my eye I see exactly what we
need to see. The target is emerging from the exit.

'Go!' Steph shouts. She's trying to get her seatbelt on but
it's stuck. I screech off at high speed sending her flying back
in her chair. Superfoods are flying all over the car, as well as
newspapers, magazines and the laptop. It's reasonable payback
for the goji berry trick!

'Ouch!' she says.

'Yeah, serves you right! Now watch that car.'

The client has told us her husband is a former army man
and highly paranoid. He will spot anyone following him a
mile off. Clients always say that: they were in the army, or they
were former policemen, racing car drivers, permanently paranoid, or all of the above. People panic a lot when they're
paying someone to follow their partner. This client was no
exception to the rule.

Here we are, going at 60 miles an hour down a country lane. Steph is tracking the route on sat nav so we can see where all the potentially problems are, any places where he might turn, or if we've got time to hang back. When we think we're coming up to a potentially tricky bit, we speed up so he's in sight. The rest of the time we have to play it cool. We can't be seen by him too much. Surveillance is certainly an art form. It still makes me panic, but not half as much as when we first started doing this job.

In total we followed the target for over an hour, which is quite a way by surveillance standards. Usually it's best to only follow for half an hour. If a journey goes on any longer, ideally we involve more cars. Unfortunately, when you don't entirely know what the target is going to do, or where they're going to go, you just have to hope for the best. Sometimes it works and sometimes it doesn't. This time, however, we pat ourselves on the backs when we've followed for over an hour without being seen and we're pulling up on a residential estate. Which is not the one where he lives with his wife!

We pull up further down the street from the target and watch as he gets out of his car, opens his boot, and retrieves an overnight bag. I activate the video camera on the dashboard.

'Interesting,' says Steph, peering through her binoculars.

'I know. Why else would you have an overnight bag except to stay over?'

'Exactly. I think this is what we call red-handed.'

Steph whips out a long-lens camera and is taking pictures.

There's a cluster of houses that overlook a small green. He uses a key to unlock a door and goes into one of them.

'Ah!' Steph puts down the camera and looks at me. 'Now what, brains?'

'Hmm. Looks like we're going to have to stay put for a bit and hope he goes out to dinner or something.' We both sit and stare at the door. In reality we should be pleased we've got a result, but so far we've proved nothing. This could be anyone's house. We're 90 per cent sure that this must be his mistress's home but because of the tragic circumstances, I'd like to be proved wrong.

Over two hours later and I've developed a case of uncontrollable wind.

'Can you PLEASE stop it! You're killing me with this stench!' Steph whines.

The weather is sunny and lots of residents are sitting outside their houses. We don't want to raise too much suspicion by opening the blacked-out windows to reveal we're inside. Two women sitting in a car on a residential estate looks dodgy, no two ways about it.

'It's those bloody little pellets of shit! The goji berries you gave me! You can deal with the consequences,' I tell her, secretly delighted that her trick has backfired – literally. Steph squeals with trauma at the smell, but there's nothing she can do about it.

'I need to get out. I can't cope. I'm going for a walk.'

'Yes! I win!' I exclaim, with utter delight. Not the most lady-like of contests, but it provides amusement for twenty minutes. I always win battles of fumigating people out of cars, because I have no sense of smell. All thanks to shoving part of a pen up my nose as a baby. Damaged all my nerve endings and nothing can ever be done about it. When Paris shoved a bead up her nose at the age of three, my mum said it was karma for all the stress I put her through with that pen.

I watch Steph walk to the end of the street and stand there. She can't go far in case the target emerges. She knows if she isn't in the car, she'll be left behind. Once Jess decided to have a wee down a back street. It was back in the very early days and she had drunk copious amounts of fluids: tea, coffee, Coke, water – you name it, Jess drank it. We'd been surveying someone for hours and hours, and for the final two hours of the mission she was in utter agony for the toilet. We were supposed to leave at 9pm exactly, so she went for a wee down a back street at 8.56pm. Then at 8.58pm the target emerged and jumped in his car. I couldn't see Jess and I couldn't risk wasting the last eight hours of work, so she was left exactly where she was. In the middle of winter in the freezing cold. It was two hours before I could get back to her, by which time she had walked over two miles to the nearest pub for refuge. Never again did she drink like she had on that job. Now she will be the last person you'll see with a bottle of water on surveillance! This is why right now Steph is well within view of me, and she can also see the house where the target is. The girl is dizzy, but she isn't quite that daft.

'Are you done yet?' she asks, peering into the car ten minutes later.

'All done. Promise,' I tell her.

'Is that the truth or a lie?'

'Um, could be either, to be honest.'

'Go for a walk yourself if you're going to do that to me again. You're not funny.'

'Yes, miss,' I quip.

'Now what are we going to do? Can't sit around here all night!' Once again she's stating the obvious.

'I know. I've reviewed the footage of him going into the house. Now I'm going to phone the client and tell her the address. It will be up to her if she wants us to stay here all night.'

'Agreed. I'll go get the house number and have another look at the door.'

I watch her trot down the path, sneakily look at the door, swivel on her heels and trot back again.

'Problem,' she says, getting into the car.

'What?'

'There are six numbers on the door. It's the entrance to apartments.'

'Bugger!' I slump back into my seat and stare at the cars in front of me.

'Yep. Now what?' I love the way she looks to me for the answers, when in actual fact she's just as good as me. If not better.

'Well … er … I know!' I've had a brainwave. 'I'm going to be an Avon lady!'

'How funny,' she says laughing. 'This I have to see!'

I get out of the car and dive into the Narnia boot to find some props. A few minutes later I'm back in my seat. I slick my long hair back into a low bun, and don a pair of dark glasses. Super-red lipstick and a blazer complement the look. As well as the obligatory clipboard, of course!

'Very impressive,' Steph says as I present my finished look for approval. 'Get out there and rock it!'

I climb out of the car and head back down the path to the front door. By now most of the residents have gone indoors, thankfully. The sun is setting and it's starting to get dark. Just as I'm heading down the path the door opens. It's them!

I have no option but to keep going. If I turn back to the car now, I'll raise more suspicion. They're coming towards me, arm in arm. Oh my lord, I hope Steph is getting this on camera. I've not even got my phone with me. I could kick myself, I'm so mad.

The target is looking me in the eye. I break his gaze by staring down at my clipboard. Thankfully I'm not the blushing type, but if I was my face would be the colour of beetroot. The mistress is giving me a very dodgy 'stay away from my man' look. She is rather attractive. I figure she must be in her forties, and has really long blonde hair with a tanned complexion. I've always wondered if people find it better or worse when their partner has an affair with a good-looking person. I suppose the answer's individual to each situation.

The couple have now passed me, and I decide to fake an 'oh dear I forgot something' moment and turn round. They don't notice as they're getting into his car together. I hang back slightly until the car has reached the bottom of the street, then I take off my heels and run, throwing myself into the driver's seat and starting the car simultaneously.

'Did you get them?' I ask Steph as we drive off.

'Sure did!'

Relief floods through me. 'Thank God for that! Was that really bad?' I ask her, looking for reassurance.

'Not at all. You looked like an Avon lady who'd lost her way … Go down there!' She points.

'Exactly the look I was aiming for.' Right now I need to get rid of this look, though. There's only the two of us on this job, so if I have to get out of the car and follow on foot wherever they end up, I can't look like the Avon lady again.

I'm pulling out the bun from my hair.

'Turn left in 100 yards,' Steph orders.

Unclipping all the hair extensions …

'Speed up, traffic lights ahead.'

Grabbing a hairbrush and whizzing it through my hair.

'Three cars ahead now.'

I reach for a pack of wipes and remove the red lipstick and most of my eye make-up. I've taken off the glasses so now, if I can just change my top when the car stops, I'll be a totally different person.

The target heads for the motorway, and I can chill out for a bit.

'Looks like he's heading for the airport,' Steph says with a confused look on her face. I say nothing, but I think she's right.

Another twenty minutes later, and the airport is exactly where we pull up.

'Are you as nervous as I am?' Steph looks worried.

'Er, yes I am.'

They park their car and I drop Steph off so she can follow them on foot.

What on earth is going to happen now? I don't know. What if he jumps on a plane and we're the last people ever to see her husband? How do we break that one to our client? As if she hasn't had enough trauma already! Do we ring her now and tell her where he is? What if we're overreacting? There are natural private investigators who can think on their feet and others who work hard for results. I'm somewhere between the two, but it feels as though this situation is being sent to try me.

I pull up the car and dig out some flip-flops so I can ditch the heels and run to the terminal. Steph texts to tell me which direction they're heading in. I fight my way through crowds of people and suitcases. Everyone's in holiday mode so they're all walking at a snail's pace. The escalator is a nightmare, and I'm getting dirty looks for trying to shove past people. Heaven forbid I should actually want to get anywhere!

I'm fighting for breath, because I'm not the most athletic person, just as I reach Steph and the target. The couple are kissing properly, not half-heartedly – this is no sister or friend – and Steph is capturing every second. I get the same rush of feeling I always get when we uncover someone being unfaithful: pleased we've got the evidence and done a good job, but sad because yet again my faith in human nature is tarnished!

'One of them is about to leave,' Steph says. I'm bent double trying to get my breath back. We're both watching intently as the soap opera unfolds in front of us.

'He got another suitcase out of his boot,' Steph tells me. 'It can't be hers because they didn't bring anything out of her house. It must have been in his car since he left the farm. He must be leaving.'

We both watch silently. In that instant, the mistress takes the handle of the suitcase from the target and they have one final kiss before she turns around and leaves – on her own. The suitcase must be hers after all.

'Thank the @£%!^&* for that!!!!!!!' Steph says, looking fit to collapse with exhaustion. I am utterly relieved. Steph turns off the camera and prepares to follow him again, while I once again set off to get to the car.

It does beg the question though – what should we have done if he'd left? Until we were sure he was going we couldn't have told the client anything. Although then it would have been too late to follow him or even find out where he was going. We didn't know he was heading to the airport until we were nearly there, so even if we'd called to tell his wife, she'd have had no time to get there. We could have been wrong and created unnecessary panic. No, for now I think we handled the situation exactly as we should have. It was a very close call though.

The next day I sit in the Tree-House and make the dreaded phone call to the client. I tell her that I'm truly sorry for everything she's gone through and the loss she's suffered. I tell her very quickly we've got the evidence she wanted. There's no point in beating around the bush. What she wants to know more than anything is whether we caught him, and we did. I tell her about how we followed him to a house and then on to the airport. I explain that he must have had the mistress's suitcase in his boot all day at work but I don't know why. I tell her they went to the airport and she left alone. The reasons why are anyone's guess. Maybe he's decided not to leave his wife? Or maybe the mistress has just gone on holiday. We can't tell her that for sure, but what we can and do tell her is that her husband is unfaithful. The question she's been wanting answered for so long. He was lying when he withdrew his confession. He was unfaithful and this must be the truth.

Our client takes it reasonably well. She's hurt, naturally, but she's relieved. She knows this is the end for them. The photos and videos are the final nail in the coffin of their marriage. You'd like to believe in mankind, and know that when awful events like the death of a child are sent to try us, we stick together. That in some way it brings us closer. But in this case, it certainly seems it tore them apart. Both Steph and I were affected by the case, and for months afterwards we still thought of that woman and wondered how she was getting on and what she was doing.

In reality, it wasn't long before she was back in touch. The story didn't end there. They did what lots of couples do: broke up then got back together several times. He carried on telling our client that his affair was over – and then that it wasn't. Her next request to us was a little more extravagant, though.

> They've both moved to Italy. They're not together, but they live two hours apart. I don't know what's going on, and my husband refuses to give me his actual address. He comes home every two weeks, but I was suspicious when I heard she lives in the same region. I don't know what to believe, but I don't want to leave him unless they're actually living together. I simply need to know.

'Pack your bags, Steph,' I trill down the phone. 'We're off to Italy!'

★　　★　　★

And what a fabulous adventure Italy was. Our days were spent eating pasta, listening to men sing on gondolas and drinking only the finest red wine … Oh, who am I kidding? I'm totally fibbing! We went to Italy and spent nearly two weeks on what seemed to be a wild goose chase, riding up and down the Italian countryside on rickety old trains, feeling sick the whole time.

The husband didn't live in a tourist city; it was authentic Italy at its most basic. We stayed in a bed and breakfast three doors down from him, and I wouldn't like to say what insects shared our living quarters with us. To say we were out of our comfort zone is an understatement. Every day we woke up praying he would meet his mistress, just so we could get our evidence and hop on the first flight back to glorious (I don't care if it rains all the time) Manchester! Instead our torture was dragged out day after day. The husband travelled over an hour and a half to work and back every morning and night. He worked, jumped on his train and went back to his authentic Italian house. Mistress was nowhere to be found. It was the most fabulously boring job that ever was. It was only a couple of weeks later that he returned home for good after his working contract had come to an end.

Looking back, I find the whole background story to this case disturbing. When such awful things happen in life, who knows how we will deal with them? The death of their child is pretty much the worst thing any parent can face. The husband's way of dealing with his pain was to have an affair. It's certainly not ideal, but if that's what he needed to do to get through it, who are we to argue? I know I've no right to talk with my history. The awful part is that our client was caught in the crossfire and had to endure even more pain thanks to his infidelity.

Thankfully, though, it seems they can now put this sad and sorry episode behind them and finally move forward together.

JUST WHEN YOU THINK
YOU KNOW IT ALL ...

I'm with Steph and we look like plant pots! We're in the Scottish Highlands somewhere near Loch Ness and we've been here for three days non-stop, wearing awful green rain macs and sitting on stools like garden gnomes. Well, almost non-stop. In the evenings, we've bolted to our log 'flaming' cabin on the side of the lake to sleep. It's cold, miserable and boring. There's no TV, no entertainment, nothing. Just us and around ten men fishing! At one point I had to stop Steph from trotting off to the local RSPCA to see if she could hire a dog to walk, just for the entertainment value.

To say we're having a 'dry' spell sounds a little awful. Having a 'dry' spell is not a very nice way to describe the fact that for the past four weeks, in every single case we've worked on, the person has been faithful. We're investigating phantom cheaters. Some might think we're lucky to be sitting here at the edge of this picturesque lake, but watching a seventy-year-old man fish, all day until nightfall, is nothing short of boring. I know it's a good thing for the guy's marriage, but wow, boring doesn't even cover it.

Very annoyingly there are no restaurants, takeaways or anything of the kind. I sent Steph to find a supermarket yesterday and she ended up making a 50-mile round trip! Thankfully we've only got a day left on the case and then we can get back home! No more sitting at the side of a lake, trying to blend in with fishermen. Where this man could find a mistress around here, I don't know!

I never thought there could be a situation in which a male detective would be better than a female. We fit in virtually everywhere, and we raise far less suspicion than any man does – but sitting here, trying to blend in, I'm finally eating my words. This is the one and only time when a man would be far better suited than ourselves.

The phone begins to ring and Steph falls off her stool. She's been napping on the job, under cover of her mac!

'Hello, The Lady Detective Agency,' I say, watching Steph pull herself back onto her stool and try to pretend nothing happened.

'Hi, I wonder if you could help.' The lady at the end of the phone is very softly spoken. I need to lower my brash Northern tones for this one.

'Of course. What would you like help with?' I try to speak gently.

'I think my husband is having an affair with a woman I know. It's a neighbour of ours, actually. We live in Buckinghamshire. I'm not totally sure if I'm right, but I strongly suspect.' I'm thinking it's an excellent location. My cousin lives in the area so I can combine it with a trip to see her.

'OK, and you'd like us to get the evidence for you, I take it?'

'I would. I can give you all the information required, but I think he should be followed after he drops me at work, if that's OK?' She is exceptionally polite.

'That shouldn't be a problem. It sounds like you've thought it through.'

The lady then continues for nearly an hour giving me the full breakdown of her marriage history. They've been married for over forty years, which by my estimation makes her somewhere around sixty. They have a large family, five children altogether. All very successful, but it seems they lost their way after the kids moved out and started their own lives. Rather sad really. Husband has become emotionally detached, and wife pines for the family that no longer surrounds her every day. Somewhere in the middle of it all she believes he's taken to finding comfort – or rather 'entertainment' – in the arms of this other woman, their neighbour.

Other woman is a beautician. As part of the investigation our client wants us to go and speak to her, try and get as much information as we can out of her. That's all very well and good, but how can you make someone tell you the truth? It just doesn't happen if they've got something to hide. So I decide to have my nails done! Beauticians like a good chatter, and asking for information in the course of a normal conversation won't seem suspicious at all. The next stage of the plan is to follow him after he drops his wife off at work, and see what he does.

'Sound a good one?' Steph asks peering out from her under mac while eating an apple.

'Possibly,' I say, then fill her in on all the details. 'We're like the grim reapers of investigation at the minute, so I won't be at all surprised if he's entirely innocent.'

'That's a fair point.' She looks around her at the beautiful scenery, then back at me like a lost puppy. 'Can we go home nowwwwwwwwwww?'

'Another three hours,' I tell her, staring straight ahead at the water.

'Oh, but …' Now she's regressed to the toddler phase. 'He's not going to do a darn thing in the next three hours except fish! Let's just run for it.'

'Er, no! We're being paid to sit here. Get over it!' I tell her firmly.

Steph huffs, but goes back to watching our target catch yet another fish.

*   *   *

A few days later and it's a stunning autumn day, the kind when you're allowed to dig out your knee-high boots and woolly jumpers. My dream is to go to New England at this time of year and check out all the stunning scenery. The leaves turning red, yellow and golden brown, and just a small chill in the air. But for now I'm going to have to stick to the normal English version, which I have to say is still stunning. We've made our way to Buckinghamshire and settled into our new home for the week with my cousin.

And now I've pulled up outside a yellow- and blue-painted beautician's, and I'm off inside to have my nails done. I've left Steph, who is currently sampling the delights of the local spa. Either way her version is going to be a lot better than mine, by the looks of the building. A bell rings when I open the front door.

'Hellooooo,' sings a lady in welcome. She's exactly like the picture I've been given. I know that sounds rather obvious, but not everyone looks like their picture. This woman does, however. She's petite, with blonde hair in a sharp bob. Rather attractive, I think.

'Hi, I'm here for my appointment,' I say. 'It's Hannah Jameson.' A name that sprang to mind when I called earlier.

'Oh hello, Hannah, lovely to meet you. We've not seen you here before.' Clearly as chatty as I expected her to be.

'No, I'm just passing through town for work.' I'm trying to be smiley and friendly.

'Wonderful, come on through and we'll get you started. So what job is it you do?' Already getting chatty, which is just what I need.

'I'm an interior designer. I've a customer here and I'm doing their lounge.' I'm good at making up stories on the spot now, so I never bother to plan them in advance.

'What a fabulous job! I'd love to do something like that.' She launches into a hallelujah chorus about her lounge, kitchen, hallway, bathroom, bedrooms, study and every other element of her home. She's asking my advice on whether stripes make a room look bigger or smaller. If purple is on the way out of fashion and if gold fittings are tacky. If there was ever a woman to lead a Spanish inquisition, she is a prime candidate. I feel utterly bombarded with questions, one after the other like pellets, but I give her my opinions on all manner of interiors so I can move the chat on to personal lives.

My phone beeps with a text, and it's Steph.

'Any joy yet? x'

I sigh, because my answer is no. Interior talk is not why I'm here.

'Aw, nothing fun then?' Chatty Bird asks, nodding towards my phone.

'Oh boyfriend trouble, you know!' I tell her. Lie number 1.4 million.

'It's been a long time since I had a *boyfriend*,' she says, laughing.

'No way! You're not old enough to be married.' Flattery always works when you're looking for information. I know for a fact she's well and truly old enough. Somewhere in her early to mid-thirties.

'Get away with you. Past it, me!' she says.

'Don't be ridiculous. You must have plenty of men falling over you!'

'Ah, I used to have a decent share of them. Not so much any more. Besides, I can't say I'm interested these days. I got married and settled down a long time ago.' She says this in a calm and possibly genuine tone.

'I get what you mean. I think the same myself, to be honest. Not going to lie. The man I've started seeing is married, but I hate it. I only found out last week, and I'm pretty hurt by it all.' I'm giving an Oscar-winning performance here, with my eyes even tearing up.

'You mean he didn't tell you he was married?' She seems genuinely shocked.

'Exactly.'

'That's dreadful! I'm really lucky I married a good guy!' Chatty Chops has a really happy, beaming smile.

'Aw, that's nice. How long have you been married?' I ask her.

'Over ten years now. We're just as happy, if not happier, than the day we got married.'

'That's so lovely,' I tell her.

'Yeah, I really did do well. God help him if he had another woman on the go. Although we're both totally anti affairs. I'd be shocked if he ever bothered. We're just happy with our normal everyday lives. Even if it sounds really clichéd.' She smiles in a contented way and I'm pretty sure I believe her.

'It's not. It's really lovely. I get scared there're no good guys out there any more.'

'I know what you mean. I hear so much about it in this game. All my friends are at it with each other, and I find it really disturbing. I thank my lucky stars every day for my husband.'

This little love fest carries on until the end of my nail session, by which time I am totally convinced the woman is in no way having an affair. She is really genuine – and I don't say that often.

I leave the salon and click back across the car park in my 'first wear of the season' knee boots, with a few leaves underfoot.

'Useless. On way back. x' I text Steph and we go back to the drawing board.

*   *   *

I have another long conversation with our client and still it sounds as though he's definitely having an affair. If it's not the beautician, it must be someone else. The more I hear from his wife, the more sure I am. He comes home hours later than he should. He turns his phone off when he's out. He would rather swallow his phone than let her see its contents. His computers and phones are password-locked like he's an MI5 employee. And he has no interest in her. He's certainly hiding something – we just need to find out what it is.

The very next day Steph and I sit in the car outside their marital home on a typical housing estate. The properties are built from a light-coloured brick; most are detached and of decent size. The gardens are all perfect, and you just know it's the kind of estate where families reside. Two-car families, with a people carrier or 4x4 alongside something more commuter-friendly parked next to it in the drive.

It's early in the morning and he'll be leaving in the next thirty minutes. The client isn't sure whether he'll be taking her to work today or not so she's asked us to follow him from when he leaves home. As it happens, they emerge and get into the car together. We're parked around the corner out of sight, but they have to pass us to leave the estate.

'He's coming,' says Steph from behind her dark sunglasses.

He turns at the next corner, and I set off at full speed. We head off the estate and he's emerged onto a motorway junction. There's a sign … a sign that puts the heebie-jeebies in me! One of the worst signs any investigator could possibly ever see. 'ROADWORKS AHEAD.'

'Oh … shit …' Steph says. She knows what's coming. We set off about ten seconds ago, and already we have a potential problem on our hands.

The motto of investigation is: the worse traffic gets, the closer you stay to your target. That then poses a whole new set of problems. Them seeing you, being too close, missing signals, all sorts. Either way, I've no option but to try and get as close to him as I can. That, however, is far easier said than done. It's rush hour, and he's emerged from the slipway into very heavy traffic. Traumatic.

'At 8am, I can do without this,' I say in my 'stressed, but don't show it' tone. Topping it off, my distance glasses are in the back seat, which Steph is now trying to reach for me. I really should wear them all the time, but always forget.

'Can you see him?' she yells from her balancing act halfway between the front and back seats.

'Do you want the truth or a lie?'

'Forget it.' She knows what the answer will be. Thankfully my glasses have been retrieved and she's back in her upright position.

The traffic in front of me is coming to a standstill. 'We can't lose him after thirty seconds!' she says.

'Screw this!'

'What are you doing?' Steph looks alarmed as I check all the cars I can see behind, and then in front.

'No coppers,' I say, and pull into the hard shoulder then zoom past the stationary traffic. I really need to stop doing this. It's becoming a habit, and an illegal one at that. I don't make eye contact or even glance at other drivers because I don't want to see them shaking their fists or giving me the finger.

'Oh … my … God,' Steph says, covering her eyes. 'I can't watch this.' Thankfully I can see the target's car about five cars ahead now, so I squeeze into the normal lane in the stationary traffic. Well, I say squeeze – I actually mean bully and barge my way back in, not giving the driver behind me a chance to stop me.

'You loon!'

'We didn't have a choice, did we?' I ask her, without requiring an answer. We spend the next twenty minutes stuck in traffic, and the calm atmosphere returns. That is, until the target comes off the motorway.

'Are you taking the piss?' Steph yells. There's another sign. More roadworks. My heart sinks. I don't need this stress.

'Well and truly not a good day,' I tell her.

'You can say that again.'

'I feel like a gladiator. Preparing to face another duel.'

'Yeah? You don't have the body of one,' Steph says laughing.

'Funny girl! Keep watching the car, tool!'

This time our contender is a dual carriageway that's been reduced to one lane. Not only that, but there's a slipway letting traffic into it. One woman attempting to join the traffic thought she could take me on and zip in front of me. Yeah, right. She didn't bank on my car being bigger and faster than hers! Irritating Woman was not best pleased and displayed her emotions with the use of her car horn, five times! The lunatic. I was rather infuriated with her for trying to cut me up, so I retaliated with my horn too.

'Not ideal this when we're supposed to be keeping under cover and all that.' Steph is well and truly in sarcasm mode. 'Er, stop now!'

Annoying Woman beeps twice more.

'OK, I'm done.' It did relieve some stress, but was not a very professional move to make.

Ten minutes down the road and we face another hazard of the job. Traffic lights. There's nothing we could have done differently. He sails through the lights, and then they turn to red.

'Noooooooooo,' Steph wails. I admit defeat, and hit the steering wheel. Of all the people we've followed, all the erratic and speedy drivers, technically this man should have been easy because he keeps to speed limits and doesn't break the law. Fate, however, has not been on our side and, officially, we've lost him. We both go into sulk mode, and stare out of our respective windows.

'Can't believe it. After all that hassle,' Steph says, dull as dishwater.

'Hazard of the job,' I sigh and accelerate when the lights go to green.

I then have to contend with the next four cars being Sunday drivers. I do my best to overtake them, but target is too far gone. We've definitely lost him. Visions run through my head. I can see him dropping off his wife and pulling up outside a brothel. Or meeting the mistress in a sleazy hotel. Either way, we've lost him. He's bound to be unfaithful. I decide I've no option but to drive in the direction he was going. We know where her work is, so we'll just head there and hope for the best. If only the client had known beforehand that he would be taking her to work, we could have started from her workplace. As usual sod's law intervened.

Ten minutes pass, and just as all hope seems lost, I catch a glimpse of a car that looks a little like his.

'Er, Steph,' I say, pointing at the opposite side of the road. She lowers her sunglasses and looks. 'What's his registration?' She immediately starts tapping on her phone and reads it out. His car passes us!

'It's HIM!' I shout.

'Turn, turn, turn!' Steph is shouting.

'I'm on the opposite side of the road!' I'm still shouting. I look all around me and wait for a car to pass on the opposite side before I spin the car in a U-turn, faster than I've ever turned a car in my life. Steph is whooping and cheering. Against all the odds, we're now one car behind him. Amazing. Relief floods over me.

'Do NOT lose that car,' she says. Stating the obvious. So much time has now passed he must have dropped off his wife already, and will be on his own.

After ten minutes we're pulling up outside his house. We've risked life and limb to follow him – or at least that's how it feels. We've never had such a difficult, but simple, job. Fate was not on our side, but we battled it and we won. So where are we ending up? Back outside his own house! Amazing.

He goes inside and we spend the next twelve hours sitting there, watching. He doesn't go out, doesn't do a thing. Doesn't go to the shops, doesn't do his garden, no work. Nothing. We clock off and return home. All that drama, for nothing.

★   ★   ★

I call the client the next day and bring her up to speed (without mentioning that we lost him for fifteen minutes). I can hear in her voice she's utterly disappointed. She wants him to be caught so that she knows the worst and can stop torturing herself with questions.

'Well, he's slipped through our fingers this time. He won't do it again,' she tells me, steadfast in her belief that she's right, and her husband is unfaithful. She books us to watch him once more.

Three days later, and we're sat outside their house again. It feels very homely to us now. We begin our day at 9am. Our client has taken herself to work, and left him at home. Thank goodness, I don't have to chase them through traffic again.

Steph and I watch two films. We have the lunch we've brought with us, consisting of wraps and salads. Then we move on to magazines, followed by games on our phones. We get to 3pm before we start to twiddle our thumbs.

'I'm SO over this man,' Steph says. 'He does absolutely nothing. If we could dish out awards for "most dirty target", "most misunderstood target", and so on, this man would certainly win "most boring target".'

I have to say, I completely agree. Sadly we don't have enough phone reception to fire up TV on our phones, or we could have staved off the boredom for another few hours by watching *Deal or No Deal* and *The Real Housewives of New York City*!

The client phones to say she's going to stay with her sister tonight, and wants us to watch him until 11pm. Fourteen hours straight sat in a car. We can't complain, work is work, but we're darn right bored. To be fair to her, it sounds a perfect opportunity. Night away from wifey, you never know what he's going to do. She seems utterly convinced that tonight is the night we're going to get him.

Rather irritatingly, we reach 7pm and there's still no movement.

'I'm literally dying for food now,' I tell Steph.

'Me too,' she says. We both look at each other like lost puppies. We weren't planning on staying this late. We were only booked to work until 4pm so hadn't given a thought to dinner and we're on a housing estate with nothing else around, not even a corner shop. All of a sudden an idea pops into my head.

'Ah ha! We'll order Chinese,' I say, really pleased with myself.

'Yeah, brains, and how do you plan to do that?' Steph doesn't seem convinced by my master plan.

'You just watch me. What do you want?' I ask her.

'Ooo, I'll have a veggie chow mein with cashews, you little magician lady you.' Clearly taking the mick.

'You mock, but watch this.' I ring directory enquiries and ask for the number of a Chinese takeaway that delivers to the postcode we're in.

'This is the daftest plan I've ever heard,' Steph mutters under her breath. I get a number and tap it into my phone.

'Yes, I'll have veggie chow mein with cashews, a sweet and sour chicken with fried rice and spring rolls please,' I tell the Chinese lady on the end of the phone. 'For delivery … It's the car that's outside house number 21 on Portland Gate Avenue. Would you like my registration?' I'm being deadly serious, but Steph won't stop laughing. 'No, not the house, the car that's outside that house … Yes, that's right, car,' I say, giving her my registration. 'Whatever you do, don't knock on that door. That's not us, we're in the car.' She is exceptionally baffled by my request, but tells me it will be twenty minutes and hangs up.

'Are you serious?' Steph asks.

'No, I just placed an order for the Easter bunny!' I tell her. 'Of course I'm serious.'

'You've officially cracked.'

'You wanted feeding, so you're getting fed, woman.'

Five minutes later the phone rings again. It's the Chinese restaurant but this time it's a gentleman, clearly the boss of the first lady, who didn't believe the order he was reading.'

'Yes, it's an order to be delivered to a car. We're working on an undercover investigation, watching someone. I can't tell you any more than that, but we're in the car and we've been here for the past ten or so hours.' I try and reason with the man, fearing I could be about to lose the Chinese dinner we so badly need. He agrees to send it, as long as I pay by card over the phone first. I'm quite happy to do so. 'Can you throw in two forks as well, please? Plastic will do,' I ask cheekily. Thankfully he says he'll oblige.

'I'll say it again – cracked!'

'It's on its way,' I tell Steph, smiling and hanging up the phone with a real sense of achievement.

A car pulls up alongside ours, and the window goes down.

'Dinner?' asks a Chinese man, holding up a white plastic bag.

'That's us!' I say.

'Exxxxcellent. So you undercover, eh?'

Oh dear, he's going to want to join in or something.

'Correct, and you're going to blow our cover,' I hint with a big smile.

'Oh yes, yes, I no blow the cover. Here you go.' And he hands over the takeaway through the two windows.

'You, sir, are a lifesaver,' I say, really darn chuffed with myself. So chuffed, I even give him a tip. He tootles off on his happy little way, and leaves us to our amazing dinner.

'I've got to give it to you,' Steph says opening her chow mein. 'Rockin' idea!'

'I know!' Very pleased with ourselves, we tuck in.

'This is *sooooo* good,' Steph says, stuffing more food in her mouth. 'Can't believe we've never done it before on surveillance jobs.'

'And it's such a simple idea too!' I agree.

Just as I do, the obvious happens – because that's what sod's law is all about.

'Oh, you're joking!' Steph says, mouth full of dinner, staring into her rear-view mirror. The target is emerging from his front door, with a dog!

'Nope, and he's dog walking. Big time your department,' I tell her.

'For goodness' sake!' She puts her dinner down on the raised console between us. Naturally this is not placed down with the gentleness of fairies. She huffs her way out of the door, but without slamming it because that would be too noisy.

I place my dinner next to hers and watch Steph walk a short way down the road, letting the target stay ahead of her and almost out of sight. Then she runs to catch him up and see what direction he's going in. With every turn she makes, I'm following in the car not far behind. This little cat and mouse game continues over the next half a mile.

Eventually it starts to turn sour, though. As Steph turns the corner to see which direction the target has taken, he's right in front of her. Picking up his dog's poo! Steph is literally on top of him. I smack my forehead with my hand. It was unavoidable, but now she has no option but to walk ahead of him and try to predict the turns he'll make. I too have had to come to a standstill thanks to an old lady crossing the road.

As I get round the corner the sight I'm faced with isn't a good one. Steph I see, but target has vanished. Poor Steph is spinning herself around in a circle, looking utterly bamboozled. My phone rings.

'Where the hell did he just go?' she asks.

'I've no idea, an old lady was crossing the road.'

'Shit, shit, shit, shit,' Steph says, stomping her feet. 'OK, leave me with it. Stay close.' She hangs up the phone.

The next thing I know, she's jumping onto the wall of a school and over the other side. I pull up at the kerb, and leap out of the car to look over the wall. She's running at top speed across the school playground to the other side. As bad as this situation is, it's quite amusing. I don't understand why we've had so much bad luck with this man. He slips through our fingers at any given opportunity.

I dash back to the car, and indicate to pull out. I need to turn back around and see if there was anywhere we went wrong, or missed him.

I check all around me, before making a U-turn in the middle of the road as fast as I possibly can. One of those slick turns like in the movies. Much slicker than the one I did when following him back from his wife's office. Only problem is, the takeaway flies all over the place. Floors, seats, carpets, even my laptop that's on the back seat. I'm horrified. It's one massive sloppy Chinese mess. Bad luck is just the way it is on this job.

I have to regain focus and go back to finding the target – and Steph! I look all around and neither of them are anywhere to be seen. I pull up and decide to wait, beginning to worry where she has got to. I try ringing her phone, but there's no answer. Then, after fifteen minutes, my phone goes. It's her.

'Where are you?' I ask.

'Not a sodding clue!'

'What?'

'I don't know! There are houses.'

'What the heck happened?' I ask her, trying to make sense of it.

'Well, I went over the school wall because it looked like a shortcut to the corner he would have taken. Although, he wasn't there either. So I tried right, then left. Then I don't really know what happened and now I'm here. Lost him.' She sounds very disappointed in herself.

'And we don't know where that is?'

'Nope.'

'OK, hang up and activate the tracker on your phone.' I tell her. We have it on all our phones now, just in case. It once saved me when I followed a target for eight hours in a car and didn't have the foggiest where I ended up, but the tracker told me.

'Oooo, good idea, brains. I'll text you. Give me a second.' She hangs up, and then sends a text telling me where she is. Not quite sure how she managed it, but she's got a serious distance away from me!

I pick her up and she is mortified at the state of the back of the car.

'What the hell did you do?'

'Don't ask!'

'All the time I was lost, I was looking forward to getting back here and finishing my dinner!' Bless her, her little eyes look hurt and sad.

We drive back to the target's house and he's in the kitchen making his tea! Clearly he did nothing – yet again. We wait there until 11pm, and another bizarre day is over. With no results.

*   *   *

Once again I ring the client, tell her the day's dramas (or lack of them), and she is still utterly convinced that we've just missed him getting up to something.

'We'll get him next time,' she tells me. It's almost as if she's sorry we've not been able to catch him for my sake. I do try to suggest that maybe he's just not up to anything, but she's convinced. There's nothing I can do to change her mind. I just listen, am there for her and do exactly what she tells me to do.

Another two weeks later, our client is back on the phone. Utterly convinced that today is the day we will catch him.

'I'm working tonight. I've spoken to our neighbour, the beautician, and she says she's going for a party with some colleagues and friends. Only I rang the place where she said she's going for dinner and they've got no bookings for over eight people, even though she says she's going with twenty of them. I know it's a lie. He's said he has to go to his brother's for dinner, but I've spoken to his brother and he's going away for two days with his work. They have to be seeing each other. Can you get one set of people watching her house, and one watching mine?'

I tell her of course we can. Her logic sounds convincing. I've told her I don't think the beautician is the right person, but it's up to her what she books us to do.

So a couple of days later we find ourselves outside their house once again. Steph and I are outside the target's location, with Jess and Helen outside the supposed mistress's house. He's not there, and she's not there. It doesn't look promising.

'I'm so over this estate now,' Steph says.

'And I perfectly agree,' I tell her. We're both staring at the same wall we've stared at for hours upon end over the past month.

Every two minutes the phone beeps with texts from Jess and Helen.

'White car leaving.'

'Astra turning the corner.'

'Black Golf turned up.'

Basically every type of car that goes near her house. Thankfully she's at the end of a cul-de-sac without through traffic, because Jess and Helen are taking today's mission very seriously. Nothing is happening. I know another member of our surveillance team, Laura, is in the area where the beautician's supposed to be having her works dinner so just on the off-chance, I ask Laura to check the car park to see if her car is there. She eventually phones through and tell us that it's not.

The beautician's not where she said she was going to be, and why would she lie? It doesn't make sense. We know he's not at his brother's either. We must have the situation wrong. They must be together.

'To be so adamant that your husband is having an affair, and to hire us so often, she must have really strong reasons,' Steph ponders.

'Whenever she speaks to me, I'm totally in her boat. I get it, I know where she's coming from and what she's talking about. Every single thing she says has lots of merit, and even *I'm* totally convinced he's up to something. Then we sit here, and it's like a gut instinct I get that I know nothing is going to happen. It's really strange. I just can't see it, and I don't know what it is.' I truly am very confused by the whole thing.

'Do you think she's paranoid?'

'No, I really don't. You know me. If I think someone's paranoid, I'd say so. I'd be talking this woman out of wasting her money – because let's face it, she's really wasted some money. I know it's not our place to judge, and we don't. But if I thought we really weren't going to find anything, I'd tell her. We don't rip people off. Sitting here for hours isn't much fun, is it?'

'That's true. I know we say it all the time. This job truly is one of the cases where you think she's right.'

We debate the issue between ourselves for over half an hour.

It's 10.58pm – and we're due to clock off at 11pm.

'I literally cannot believe this. Once again, another attempt and we've found nothing. I'm really mad though. Where the hell is he?'

'Anything? x' I text Jess.

'Not a thing. We off at 11? x' is her reply. It's a tough call to make. I need to ring the client and give her my best advice. We need to tell her what to do.

There's a chance that if we leave, they could return together. Not very likely, to be fair. If they are having some kind of an affair, they probably won't come back to either of their marital homes together. However, considering they live literally around the corner from each other, the chances are if they've been together they will both return at similar times. That won't be proof, but it will tell us we're in the right ball park. Can we leave not knowing where either of them is? Surely we have to stay? That being said, I don't want the client wasting any more time. The frustration is immense.

I decide to lay the facts out very simply for her.

1. We leave, they return at similar times and we don't find out about it.
2. We leave, they return together and go to one or the other house and we don't find out about it.
3. We stay, and it costs her more wasted money.

In the end she decides that we've come so far, we'll take it hour by hour. In for a penny, in for a pound and all that. I feel really sorry for her when she talks about it being like an addiction. I know exactly what she means. It's like she's getting a fix, spying on her spouse. Like a gambler that just keeps feeding the addiction, but she has to keep on spying.

11.14pm and Steph is rooting around in the boot for an old crossword book she put in there. Only problem is, there's so much junk she's been back there for over ten minutes. I'm looking in the rear-view mirror laughing at her, when the target's car pulls up directly in front of me. He's back. It dawns on me really quickly that there's no room on his driveway because his daughter's car is there, even though she's gone out. We shouldn't have parked so close. What's he going to do? He's taking his time getting out of the car. Steph is aware of what's happening in front and is now hovering around the boot. Under no circumstances can he see her, because she came face to face with him in the dog poo incident. Currently she's trying to shield her face with the lid of the boot, while still watching. I'm literally holding my breath, trying to look as if I'm talking into my phone. He is directly in front of the car. If he turns around he'll see me, and possibly Steph. This is the first moment in a long time I've been nervous.

He gets out of his car, and leans back into the driver's side for something. I can't see what. Is he talking to someone? Is another woman going to emerge from the passenger seat? He walks to the back of the car and I'm shielding my face as best I can. I notice the boot of the car has been closed and there's no sign of Steph. I'm worried she's dived under the car to hide. What if I have to set off in a hurry and I run her over? Oh goodness … He opens the boot of his own car, and gets out – ASDA BAGS! Not one, not two, three, four or five. NINE Asda bags! The man has been and done the weekly shop! He takes it all inside and that's the end of that. No mistress, no nothing. Asda! Why the hell did he lie?

Jess and Helen concluded their night of surveillance an hour later, when supposed mistress returned drunk as a skunk, from a night out – with her husband.

We're baffled! Utterly baffled. The man's mistress was Asda!

* * *

We watched that client's husband another four times in all, and he never put a foot wrong. We advised her that we don't think he is doing anything, but we'll be there to do whatever she tells us to do. It's not our place to argue. Even now she's totally convinced that we've just missed the day when he's been up to something. I suppose it's possible but fate would have to be working in a very mysterious way. Maybe he does have a mistress somewhere – who knows? One day she is sure we will catch him. I don't know.

Months down the line, though, the one thing I know for a fact, because everyone tells me when they get in my car, is that there's still a very faint whiff of Chinese takeaway!

THE BEAMING
SMILE FAMILY

It takes over two years to settle my divorce case and it's drama I could do without. Since we got together, Ben has been a rock about it. Every time I've had to go before a judge and see James, he's been right by my side. Regardless of the date, he moves his shifts at work, puts his life on hold and makes sure he is there to support me – and thank goodness he does.

But when the final judgment comes through, the upshot is that I lose the barn house that I redeveloped and James is having it repossessed. Ultimately there is nothing I can do to save it. Every penny I had was in that house, and now it's all gone. I built it from scratch and really hoped I'd be able to live in it and bring Paris up there. I knew every single inch of that house. I'd picked every fixture and fitting. Paris said her first words in that house, and took her first steps. She chatted to the sheep in the fields every day, and it became our haven while my marriage was crumbling. Now it is just bricks in the middle of a field that is no longer mine.

I come out of the court with tears in my eyes. It's awful to lose it, and the money too. But part of me feels relieved. Is it relief that it is all over, and there will be no more court battles?

I can officially divorce now, and be free. Free to start my life all over again. Or is my sadness because I have nothing to show for what I worked for? In today's economy, I've no idea how I'll ever get back on the property ladder. I'm well and truly back at square one. Before today I'd gone back lots of squares in life, but now there are no more squares I can go back to and I'm stuck in God's Waiting Room with the parents for the forseeable future! I take Ben back to see the house one last time. We walk around the grounds and look over the hills. I sit on a rock and watch the world go by. I am only a few feet away from where we had a huge bouncy castle for Paris's second birthday, and all the family came. She ran around for hours, laughing and giggling. It was a wonderful day. Just one of the many memories that would be going with this house. The winters when I'd been snowed in because the drive was too long to clear all the snow. The two months I'd attempted to live on the site in a static caravan while it was being built. The winds were so bad at night I was convinced it was going to blow the caravan over and I'd die. Even just the summers when I'd leave every door and window open to blow in the summer breeze was a beautiful memory. It was the home where my marriage ended, but that doesn't spoil all the good times I had there with Paris. I look down at Ben from my rock and everything fits into place. He's my life now. Yes, there are memories here but it's time to move on. There are more memories to be made, truly happy ones, and this is not the place to do it. He stands in the courtyard with his hand on his hip, and I just want to jump down from my rock, run and kiss him.

After all, let's face facts. That house came with a whopping mortgage, the grass was always taller than my car because

I could never be bothered to have it cut, the private water system would freeze up when the temperature got below five degrees, the satellite dish blew down all the time because it was in the middle of nowhere, you couldn't walk to a shop, three bathroom tiles would always fall off no matter how many times they'd been put back, I could never be bothered to get the balcony put on so the doors out of my bedroom led to a six-foot drop, the bottom of the driveway flooded for fun, the neighbours didn't like me, the underfloor heating never worked in three rooms, I never liked the colour I painted the office but couldn't be bothered to change it and there was sheep shit everywhere!!!

From that moment everything is a little easier. I turn and leave the house for the final time, and although there might be a tear in my eye, I don't look back.

★   ★   ★

Finally, I'm a divorcee. And it's not long before I have some exciting news. I'm not going to lie and I just can't hide it. (There's a song in there somewhere!)

One summer's day in 2011, when we have been seeing each other for about eighteen months, Ben plans a whole day of activities for Paris, him and me. First of all we have a lovely lunch and then we go for a walk. He has found a beautiful walking spot, one I hadn't even known existed. There are two lakes right next to each other, surrounded by forestry and hills. We find a spot to sit down on a bridge between the lakes, and it is as if we are literally on the water. It's amazing. In reality we aren't very far away from home, but it's so picturesque we could be in the depths of Scotland.

Next thing I know, Ben is whispering something to Paris and she is beaming.

He's probably just told her he's got sweeties, I decide. Then she begins to speak. 'Er, Mummy, when are you going to marry Daddy?' I look at her in amazement and she's still beaming. So is Ben.

'Well?' he asks. He is deadly serious. I am utterly floored but accept immediately.

'Of course I'll marry Daddy!'

Paris jumps up and does a little dance around us while Ben gives me the best kiss of my whole life. Now we are the beaming smile family!

He pulls a ring box out of his pocket, which he opens to reveal the biggest monster of a ring I've ever seen. He's designed it himself – a huge blue stone surrounded by diamonds. Exceptionally me. The man knows me far too well. It is the most amazing ring anyone could have ever picked.

'OOOoo shiny,' Paris coos over it. 'I like it, Mama. Does this mean I can be a bridesmaid?' Paris always gets her priorities straight!

How can a man get a proposal so right? There's no cheesy drama, just our little family together in a beautiful setting – and it was really clever of him to involve Paris, the most important person in all of this. I couldn't have planned it better myself. It sounds really darn clichéd, but if ever my stomach filled up with happiness, this is the time. I've never felt so content and fulfilled. I think there's certainly one thing to be said for being divorced. When you've done it the first time and got it so wrong, it's even better second time around when it's so very right!

WHEN CLIENTS MESS WITH YOUR HEAD!

There are some clients you feel a real connection with. It doesn't happen very often any more, and that makes me scared that I've become immune to the crazy train we ride on. But one of those clients is John.

We've had a lot of male clients in the past who worry what their wives are up to, but there is something about John that really gets to me. Not just me, but the other ladies too, and they've never even spoken to him! Maybe it's because he's so level-headed – a professional man who is truly tortured by his relationship. Or at least, after what feels like a million phone calls, that is the conclusion I've come to. In reality I am involved in his life for only a couple of weeks, but during those weeks I feel I truly get to know him. We take him into our world, and he takes us into his. Part of me worries when I become attached and start to care about clients. It's not my place. I don't entirely know what's going on, but sometimes they just get to you! For that reason, I simply have to tell you his story ...

★   ★   ★

It's a cold and rainy morning up North. A truly stereotypical Northern day. Miserable, cold, and a day when all you want to do is get under a duvet and never move. Instead I'm in the Tree-House. My Starbucks skinny latte with caramel has gone cold, and I'm all alone. I'm debating making a run for it – jumping in the car and running home to bed. I can't focus, my brain is simply not in gear today! I'm trying to understand how to search-engine optimise our website, which is just as boring as the description makes it sound. I type three words and stare out of the window. I type two more and stare some more. This pathetic working effort continues for the next hour. When I hear the phone ring, I just stare at it for a while before my brain registers that I need to actually answer the damn thing. Oops.

'Hello, The Lady Detective Agency,' I say sounding very flustered.

The voice on the other end of the phone is a man, and he sounds very serious. No messing with this one, I think!

'My name is John, and I need to talk to you about my wife, Stacey.'

'Of course, fire away.'

'I think she may be having an affair with someone from her country club.'

'What makes you think this?' I ask, getting straight to the point.

'I don't entirely know, but she lies about a lot of things. Something just isn't right. It's been going on for months. I have a feeling, but I can't prove anything.'

'What kind of things is she lying about?'

'Everything and nothing. Where she is, what she's doing, when she's coming home. She's always late, and generally very narky and unhappy.'

I don't feel able to draw any kind of conclusion so far, so I just keep listening. 'What I need you to do is follow her next week. She's got an event with some of the country club residents. They're going for a meal in Birmingham, having drinks and staying at a hotel that night. I'm going to be looking after our little girl, so I just need to know exactly what she's doing.'

'Of course, that's no problem. I'll check our staffing levels and see what I can do, but I'm sure we can sort out something.'

'I could be entirely wrong, but I think her affair is with the owner of the club. She mentions him a lot, and I saw a text from him on her phone a couple of weeks ago. When I asked her about it, she'd deleted it and said I must have been imagining it. I know I wasn't, so that makes me suspicious.'

Hmm, interesting.

'I've been taking notes on everything that's happened for quite some time now. I'm away a lot but I always keep records. I can get them emailed over to you by my assistant if you wish?'

Assistant, huh? I wonder what this guy does for a living. I don't ask because I don't like to pry. Even though it may seem a very ordinary question, you never know how much a client wants to reveal. They could see mentioning what they do for a living as too much information, and then start to close up. Best to listen and not ask any question that doesn't directly relate to the case.

'That sounds like it could be very helpful. Feel free to send them over. What I'll do now is check who's available next week, and email you some prices. You have a think, and if you want to go ahead, email me the details, your notes and photographs of the people concerned, if possible.'

'That's fine. I'll wait to hear from you.'

We say our goodbyes. I immediately pick up the phone and call Steph. I tell her everything John has just said, and ask if she is free the following week, which she is. Then I think about the operation ahead.

Night-time surveillance is a total and utter nightmare. People drive me utterly crackers the way they leave a pub and jump in a taxi. We're then left to follow them like headless chickens, whizzing around cities I've never been in before and getting lost. This time, I'm not going to be put in that position. We're going to be exceptionally well prepared. Four of us will go and we'll work in teams of two, one always with a car and the other on foot. Steph, Jess, Helen and I can do it.

Later on that evening, I send over the quotation and John agrees the price. He sends me over his notes on his wife's behaviour and when I open the email I see it is pages and pages long. I read the first page and decide I need back-up – and alcohol. I grab my phone and tell Steph I am sending her over some information on the job. Then I get a glass of wine from the kitchen and sit in front of the computer.

'Are you kidding me?' Steph replies when she sees the length of the file.

'Nope. Have fun! Take notes, digest, you never know what will be useful.'

'I hate you,' was her reply. She loves me really.

Fifteen minutes later and I've been distracted by the daily soap operas on television when there is a knock at the door.

'If I'm doing this, you're doing it with me,' Steph says as she barges over the threshold.

'Come on in then …'

She has already swanned past me and into the kitchen to get herself some wine. I resume my place on the sofa. Steph comes through from the kitchen, pinches the television remote that's next to me, and hits the 'off' button.

'Focus, Rebecca.'

'Yes, miss.' I reach for the laptop and drag it onto my knee. 'Right.'

We both sit silently reading, and commenting every time something takes our interest.

'Three hours late home from work and she walks in pretending nothing's happened. What's that about?' Steph remarks, pointing at the screen.

'Yep, strange.'

'Comes home from work wearing a different outfit than the one she went out in, AND the zip on her trousers is undone. What?'

'Also she was very defensive when asked about it. If there was an innocent explanation, surely she'd just tell him what it was? Yep, very strange.'

I go into the kitchen to get the rest of the bottle we've opened.

'Oh, this is interesting …' Steph shouts from the living room, walking into the kitchen with laptop in hand. 'She said she was going out. He was working in London and rang her a couple of times up until 2am. The next day she called him and said she got in at 10pm and went straight to bed. BUT she got a parking fine in Birmingham at 1am, in a place which is forty-five minutes away from her home. He was the one who opened the letter, and he didn't immediately tell her. He asked her again what she was doing that night and she stuck to the original story about being in bed at 10 …'

Steph lowers her head back to the screen, utterly engrossed. 'There's more … The pair of them are out having lunch at a pub when one of her friends approaches the table and asks wifey if she had a good time the other evening when she saw her at O'Marley's bar in Birmingham. Wifey denies it was her the friend saw, but friend insists it was and claims she even saw her new car in the car park. Wifey still sits there denying it.'

'Oh my goodness.' There's certainly a chain of lies adding up here, but most of them could be explained away somehow.

I shake my head, frowning. 'Another day she said she was at her mum's, so John rang mum's – and guess what?'

'She wasn't there?' I ask.

'Exactly! Here's another. She told him she was going out with work friends one evening, then the next day said it was a different group of friends and denied ever saying it was work friends. Whenever he questions her, or tries to clarify anything, she goes mad at him.'

'I never like people who do that. They've always got something to hide,' I say.

'Won't ever let him see her phone.'

'Classic.'

'She went to Glasgow with work, but gave him the wrong hotel name. He asked who she'd gone with. She refused to answer and kicked off at him again.' Steph's determination to get to the truth is passing, and now she seems more sad than puzzled as she relays the facts. 'A random number texts her phone with a message asking how she enjoyed last night. She doesn't know he's seen the message, and when he brings it up later asking whose number it is, she denies she ever got a text.'

We're now back on the sofa, and I'm watching Steph reading from the screen and slurping my wine.

'Later she admits that a couple of men have been texting her, and one was a bit of an old flame.'

'What? She denies and possibly lies about everything else then admits to that? How strange.'

'Few weeks later, a friend of John's texted him to say he'd just seen wifey going to the doctors. When John asked her, she denied it.'

'List is pretty endless then!' I say, as Steph closes the computer and reaches for her wine. I look at her and see she's not her usual upbeat, quirky self. 'What's up with you?' I ask. 'Stephanie!!!!! Is that a *tear* I see?'

'Shove off!'

I can't help but giggle at her. 'It is! Oh my goodness, what's wrong with you?'

'It's so sad.'

'Awww, you big geek.'

'It is!' she protests. 'He's being tortured!'

'You don't know that.'

'I can tell, it's obvious. This list goes on and on, and you can see from all his writing that he's devastated about it.'

Steph doesn't usually get emotional about work but this time she really is. She's staring at the blank TV screen.

'OK, come on now, let's get a grip.' She glances at me out of the corner of her eye. 'We don't know the full story, and we have to base our investigation on facts and evidence. I mean …' I open the computer again.

1. Three hours late home from work – so she worked late.
2. Comes home wearing a different outfit. Maybe she spilt something on the other one.
3. Zipper undone. Accident.

4. Her going out and not telling husband. She didn't feel comfortable saying she'd been out.

5. Constant lying because if she admits to one lie, everything else looks like a lie so she carries on lying to cover herself.

6. When the friend saw her out – same reason she didn't tell him about the previous night out.

7. Glasgow hotel problem. She got confused.

8. Old flame texting her – strange, but she did admit it without prompting.

'I don't care,' Steph insists. 'I still think she's up to no good.'

'Put it this way – we're soon going to find out.'

The next day, sitting in the Tree-House, we spend a serious amount of time weighing up the situation. It transpires that we're split into two camps. Steph and Jess are on the side of her being unfaithful while Helen and I are undecided. The funny thing about this case is that Steph and Jess are so adamant that they are right. Usually we allow for the unexpected because in this job we can never take anything for granted. I can't remember any other time when they've been so certain of the outcome. Personally, I'm utterly baffled. It makes no sense. If she's not lying, the things she's not lying about are ridiculous and there must be innocent explanations behind them. I can't turn around and say right now, 'Yes, she is unfaithful,' because I've learned not to judge.

The detailed information John has sent has made us really connect to the story, and to him. It's like a strange jigsaw puzzle we need to put together. I think Steph feels like she knows him now! It's useful having this volume of notes instead of just a chat on the phone. I wish everyone would take a leaf out of his book and do the same!

'I'm really curious about one thing, though,' Helen chirps up from the laptop, while reading all the information for the second time.

'Fire away!'

'What job does he do that makes him travel so much?'

'Very good question, actually. I've got absolutely no idea.'

What then follows is another debate session, lasting thirty-two minutes to be exact. I wonder what's wrong with us? We never spend so much time going backwards and forwards over every tiny detail of a case! At last, we have the bright idea of Googling him and find out he is a top international barrister. All the carefully prepared notes make much more sense now.

By the day of our surveillance mission, we've talked about him so much that we feel as if we've known John for a lifetime. We're all geared up for the challenge. We want to know, possibly as much as John does, what his wife is up to.

The setting and scenario are perfect. Apparently she's going out in Birmingham with the country club regulars. At least ten people will be attending, going for dinner and then staying overnight in an amazing hotel. If she is ever going to be unfaithful, this is the ideal opportunity.

We explore the hotel earlier in the day and have a look round at all the exits, entrances and the restaurant. Apparently the group's booking is for 8pm. Next we split into two cars and head over to her office. It's a huge building, and it takes us over half an hour checking out all the car parks that are associated with it. Her car is nowhere to be found. We're kicking ourselves. This could be a problem. John has told us she usually finishes work around 5pm, and we've headed over at

2pm just in case she decides to leave early in preparation for the evening. We've had confirmation from John that he's spoken to her within the last ten minutes, and she said she was still at work. Lie number one.

Steph dials the number of the office. 'Hello' she says in her cheery voice to whomever is on the other end of the line. 'Is it possible I could speak with Stacey Holden please? ... No problem ... Thank you.' Steph turns to us. 'She took the day off!'

'Wonderful.' Jess states the obvious.

We all know what this means. It's no one's fault, just one of those things. We knew she might leave early, but we never thought she would not even turn up. In a perfect world, we would have watched her leaving home this morning, spent all day outside her work and then followed her into the evening. However, that would have involved an overnight fee for the previous night, and potentially hours of wasted surveillance. It would have bumped the client's fee up a silly amount for what in reality should be a small job. Surveillance from 2pm, when she was finishing at 5pm should have covered the situation! But it hasn't ...

'Now what do we do?' Helen asks.

'The obvious, I guess. We head to the hotel, and loiter for a really long time, keeping our fingers and toes crossed.'

'For goodness' sake!' Steph is stressed. She sits staring out of the window into the distance until we're back at the hotel.

We drive around the streets near to the hotel, trying our best to find her car. It shouldn't be too hard to find, being a top-of-the-range white Jaguar sports car with black wheels. Luckily, it doesn't take too long. Very irritatingly, it's not parked in the hotel car park but on a side street that's between four hotels! Technically she could be in any one of them, but we don't want to split up and watch all of them. For now we have to hope for the best, and assume she is staying at the one we've been told she's in.

'Ahhhh, this is messing with my head,' says Helen. 'If she is staying at this hotel, where she says she is, then maybe she is telling the truth about everything and it can all be explained away. Why would she be staying at the hotel where she's told her husband, but be up to no good? She wouldn't.'

We stare at Helen, because she's clearly just having a conversation with herself. She's asking herself questions, and then answering them.

I make an executive decision – something I don't have to do very often, considering their investigative skills are exceptional and easily as good as mine.

'We're going to the hotel where she says she's staying.'

'Can I try and con the concierge into telling me what room she's in?' Jess asks.

'No.'

'Can I ring the hotel and ask to speak to her?' she persists.

'No. It's all too dodgy. Concierge or reception would then probably ring her and say there was a missed call. If they do and she's up to no good, she will scarper sharpish. Right now we're not desperate, but if we're still here in the same position with nothing else to do at 11pm then you can crack on. Until that point, we're going to man every exit and entrance and hope for the best. Long shot, I know, but right now we can't risk anything else.'

They look like they're sulking, my little bunch of toddlers.

We all take our positions. There are only three exits so I put one person on each and float between the three of them for the next three hours. All are equally as bored as each other, and the concierge staff are checking us out. Any person who stays rooted in one spot for a few hours is bound to raise suspicion. Over the course of our time in the agency, we've got used to it. In the beginning it used to scare us, and make us think we were about to be caught out at any second. Now we have a book of excuses as long as our arm and if anyone stares at us, we smile, which confuses them!

When I glance in Steph's direction, I realise she has a problem. Three men have descended on the area where she's sitting. At first she seemed fine, but now as I'm watching she looks like she's developed some uncontrollable twitch! She's scratching her ear, ruffling her hair, her arm shoots up, and lots of other daft signals follow. I decide to go over, and she looks exceptionally relieved.

'Alright love?' I say, sitting down.

'Of course. These lovely men want to know if we will go out with them this evening. They tell me they're Arabian princes.'

'Blimey. We've not encountered any of those before,' I tell them with my eyebrows raised.

They say they will take us out for the night of our dreams, whatever that means. I decide not to ask in case it signals that we're remotely interested.

'We'd love to, but I'm afraid we've made other plans with our husbands. Unfortunately I don't think they'd take too kindly to us going out with Arabian princes, no matter how charming you are,' I say, flashing a smile. They look to Steph for some kind of confirmation.

'Sorry, gentlemen,' she tells them, shrugging her shoulders.

Out of the corner of my eye, I see our target walking down the staircase. Steph sits bolt upright and reaches for her phone to text Jess and Helen to tell them to make their way to the car. I get up and walk to the car, while Steph stays to keep an eye on the target and make our excuses to the Arabian princes.

Jess and Helen are already waiting in the back of the car when I get outside. The target emerges with Steph a short distance behind her. The target is on her own but talking on her phone. We wait until she's out of sight.

'Turn left onto Manchester Street,' Steph texts, then keeps sending us instructions at every junction until the target arrives at a restaurant.

As soon as we pull up outside, Steph jumps in the back of the car, while Jess and I head into the restaurant. Steph can't be seen inside the restaurant just in case the target noticed her on the way there.

Jess and I sit near the entrance to the restaurant, in a posi-tion where we can clearly see the target waiting at the bar. All the build-up and this is it? Is she going to be dining here with ten people? I survey the room and don't see any large tables reserved. There are a couple of men, and a couple of women sitting at individual tables looking like they're waiting for someone. Who is our target going to dine with?

The waitress is checking her chart, and my video camera, that looks like a car key, is sitting on the table recording. The wait seems to take forever, and Jess and I are finding it hard not to stare.

The target moves towards the side of the restaurant, where she takes a seat at a table for two. With no one. Great. How brilliant is that? We both sit twiddling our thumbs staring into glasses of Coke the waitress brings us, and fifteen minutes go by.

'Please don't tell me she's been stood up,' says Jess in her sing-songy voice. She's tapping her beer mat on the table and I snatch it away from her.

'Enough!' I tell her.

Jess folds her arms, and looks up in a huff. Toddler is back.

Steph and Helen are getting impatient too. They're constantly sending me texts asking what's happening.

Suddenly a dashing young man walks into the restaurant. Tall, dark and seriously handsome. He looks at least ten years younger than our target.

'Oh helloooooo,' says Jess as he walks past us. 'He is AMAZING!' I start thinking Jess may begin to drool at any moment. I turn around without looking too obvious to see where he's going.

'I don't mind following him,' she tells me. 'You know, only if you really need me to.'

'Will you please get a grip of yourself, or I'll find a bucket of ice to throw over you,' I tell her.

'Oh my. Are you kidding me?' Jess says, while staring straight past my shoulder.

'What?' I ask, not wanting to turn around for fear of being obvious.

'He's here to meet our target!' Jess doesn't seem too thrilled.

I stand up and make my way to the toilets which are directly behind them. I switch my phone to video record so I can get some evidence for our client. I have to admit, it was exceptionally easy.

I wait around in the toilets for a few minutes, faffing as per usual, before going back to Jess. I stand at our table for a short time, while playing back the footage I've just taken. Jess is still gawking at the beautiful mystery man our target is with.

'I've got it. Let's get out of here,' I tell Jess, who is just about managing to tear herself away. I hit the send button on the video, and it makes its way to our client.

Jess and I throw ourselves back in the car to the amazement of Steph and Helen.

'Well, what's happened?' Helen asks us.

'What's happened is that she's having a cosy candlelit dinner with the most beautiful man on earth, that's what's happened!' Jess tells them.

'I knewww it!' Poor Steph is horrified. 'So he was right? She is cheating on him?'

'We could be jumping to conclusions, but they look rather friendly to me!' I tell her.

I move the car into a position where I can see the restaurant door, and my phone beeps. It's the client with a response.

'That's her ex-boyfriend!' is his reply. Steph is reading over my shoulder.

'Nooooo! Poor John!' Now the girl is howling like a wolf to the moon. Steph slumps back into her seat in a huff.

'Yep, it's her ex-boyfriend,' I confirm to the ladies, who all look utterly defeated by the news.

'I had such high hopes for this one too,' Helen says.

'Sad, but we've got a job to do!' I tell them, trying to bring some order back to the situation.

'When they come out, we'll follow as far as we can in the car, but if they go down any one-way streets you pair need to jump out,' I tell Helen and Steph. Enough time has now passed since the target last saw Steph and in theory we should be OK.

They emerge a couple of minutes later.

'What the bloody hell are they doing now?' Helen asks, craning her neck to see, while Steph cracks open a packet of her favourite cheesy Doritos.

'Want one?' Steph asks thrusting the bag under my nose.

'No thanks!' I say, but Jess grabs a handful.

'Doritos solve all problems,' Steph says, still with a sulky air to her voice.

'They're going down that alley,' Jess points out.

'Oh crap!' Steph opens the door to leap out, and Helen is poised to follow, balancing on the edge of her seat.

'What are they doing?' asks Jess.

'Talking … and laughing … a lot!'

Steph is ready to run down the alley after them, but I tell her to get back in.

'In, out, in, out,' she moans. 'I'm literally going to get the best evidence I've ever got in my whole life to catch this woman out.' Steph has nothing but determination in her voice now, but it quickly subsides to boredom … 'It's been eighteen minutes now.'

'Could they be doing dirty things?' Helen asks. None of us dares answer the question, but considering Steph has them in her sights and says nothing, we all assume that's a 'no'.

Eventually they emerge from the alley, and start to walk towards a main road. We follow them in the car and watch as they go into a pub. It's a busy place so we all go in together and tuck ourselves quietly in a dark corner, still watching their every move. Not that they make many moves – they are just totally engrossed in conversation with each other.

'What do you think this is?' asks Helen.

'I'm not sure, to be honest,' I tell her.

'Me neither,' says Jess.

'If you knew nothing else, you'd just think it's two friends on a night out,' Steph says.

'The problem is we know more than that.'

As I'm talking, my phone beeps. It's John. His wife has just been in touch, telling him she's out with everyone from the country club. What the heck?

'John says she texted that she's having a great time with everyone, and made references to other people. People who aren't here.'

'What, you mean country club people?' Jess asks, confused.

'Country club people,' I confirm.

'Why on earth is she lying if there's nothing to hide? It makes no sense.'

'Exactly. How can this be anything other than an affair?'

'We can't say one way or the other, can we? They could just be meeting up for old times' sake,' muses Helen.

'It would all make sense though,' says Steph.

We continue to survey them for the rest of the evening, in and out of pubs and clubs, until we eventually follow them back to the hotel. We sit in the car filming them walking in, then switch off the camera. Thanks to the hotel security, we can't get in at this time of night to see if they go into the same room.

'That was really damn weird. I think I'm even more confused than ever now,' says Helen – and I have to agree with her. By rights, if the wife has nothing to hide, she'd have told her husband, but she and the ex didn't touch, kiss or do anything physical. Baffling to say the least.

*   *   *

A few weeks later we catch up with John. The situation has got even worse for him. We gave him all the evidence we had, but no conclusions can be drawn except that his wife is a liar. She does nothing but lie, all the time. Small lies, big lies, every kind of lie imaginable. They've not stopped in the weeks that have gone by, and are only getting worse.

Throughout the whole process John's been telling us that he loves his wife and wants nothing more than to be with her. He doesn't want their family to be broken up. He wants us to prove she is totally innocent and give him an explanation for her behaviour. To be honest, I still don't know if she has been unfaithful or not. All I want and hope for is that she can explain all the lies she's left in her path. To stop his torture, and just be truthful.

That doesn't seem very likely, though. Eventually, John tells us, he snapped. He'd had enough. Which is not very surprising, to be fair. He was at the end of his tether. How can you cope when you never know if the person you love most in the world is constantly lying to you? He tells us that he couldn't sleep anymore, and would often wake at 5am and not be able to go back to sleep. One morning, when their daughter was at his parents' house, he sat at his kitchen table, in the dark, for four hours straight, before he finally went to his car and got the evidence we'd given him.

He sat with it on the kitchen table until his wife came down for breakfast. Calmly he sat there and said nothing until she finally picked it up and realised what it was. Stacey placed the evidence back on the table, went upstairs and packed her bags. No explanation, no nothing. The two of them didn't exchange a single word. I'm convinced it was because he was just too broken to even speak any more. She walked out of their house, and never went back.

Eventually they began to speak but Stacey never gave him an explanation, and so we and John can only assume that she was having an affair with her former boyfriend. Not that she admitted that – she told John there was one reason for their now impending divorce … She could never forgive him for not trusting her.

A few days after our catch up I get an email from John. He is once again off on a trip overseas and has just boarded a plane. He's sitting in first class getting ready to turn off his computer when he sends it.

The email thanks us for our help over the past couple of months, which has been one of the most difficult periods of his life. He also says that he hopes this is the beginning of a fresh start for him. I totally, thoroughly believe it is. No one deserves what this man has been going through, to live with lies and uncertainty. To have your head messed with every single day. He doesn't know it, but that's exactly what the case has done to us. It totally and utterly baffles us, and it disturbs us how much we care about it.

I read the email to Steph, who is sitting with me, and once more she's got a lump in her throat. Our work is over and we have to let John go, but we'll never forget him.

THE ULTIMATE CHOICE

It's 6am and that time of morning when the birds are just starting to sing. I wish I could still sleep – after all, I am one of the breed of people who utterly loves sleep – but I can't. It's totally impossible. I've been sitting here for the last three hours, silent. I've not even gone to make myself a cup of tea. I'm so caught up in my thoughts I don't want to move. I never thought I'd be in this position. I've had dilemmas in life before, but I've never truly felt as much pressure as I do now.

Since we got engaged, Ben's bosses in the police force have found out what I do for a living and they're not happy about it. Basically they want me to stop, in case it could be compromising for Ben. They worry that he might be put in a difficult position if I ask his advice about a case, or if he mentions something about his work that I use in mine. In reality, we never talk about cases we're working on, but they seem adamant. But how can I simply give up The Lady Detective Agency?

To a lot of people their job is just that – a job. To me, it's a way of life. I've never had a career in which I've totally felt at home and settled. I love everything about it: the clients, the work and the girls I work with. It's a dream job, that once was just a dream but I made it work. By rights it should never have worked.

I started this journey on a whim, if I'm honest. It was a 'let's try it and see' moment. We only made it work because of the sheer hard work and dedication of everyone involved, me included. I live it, I breathe it and it is *me*. This is who I am. To sell the company would feel like selling my soul – and possibly to the devil. I'm always criticising other detective agencies who use women to front them as a marketing gimmick but give the jobs to the boys. If I sell it, my company could now become one of them. I'm cheating everyone who believes in us.

At the moment, we are everything we say we are. We're a group of women who started this journey to help others. We've done our job exceptionally well because we really do care. We don't calculate the cash, and we certainly don't rip people off. We charge what we have to in order to get the job done. Someone else could get hold of my company and turn it into a money machine. They wouldn't care about the clients like we do. How can I do it to them?

I genuinely don't want to take this step. But on the other side of me is the man of my dreams. He's lying next to me fast asleep, and his face has never looked more beautiful. I just look at him and fill up with love. I never could have imagined that such a perfect person existed. How to put into words what he is, and what he's done for me, is an exceptionally difficult task. Single-handedly he has restored all the faith and trust in human nature that I lost. I'm so thankful that I found him, I could literally cry.

When I separated from Paris's father the biggest fear in the subconscious of not just myself but everyone around us was:

who comes next? My history with men was atrocious. They were all wrong in one way or another. What if I met someone who was amazing, but didn't want children? What if I met someone who told Paris off all the time? What if he was only around for me? No one could possibly love her like I do. I'm her parent, and she is part of me. A new partner could resent her for being part of my ex-husband – but we never got any of that. Ben loves Paris unconditionally, exactly as he would his own child. I know that because I see it; he doesn't have to say it. He doesn't look at her and see my ex-husband; he looks at her and sees himself, and me! They are everything my dad and I are – they're best friends as well as father and daughter.

I often wake up in the morning to find they've snuck downstairs to have 'daddy boo' time watching cartoons together. When she cries, she runs to him. She draws pictures of them together in the park. She still has a few scars that I believe stem from her past. She has a recurring nightmare that sometimes wakes her in the middle of the night, and she will scream hysterically and cry her eyes out. It is always the same exact dream, in which Ben, my parents or I have taken her to the park and left her there. She's terrified that one of us will leave her. My beautiful daughter has no other fears in life, except that one of the people she loves most in the whole world will one day walk away. It breaks my heart and I know where it's come from.

When she has her dream, the first person to run to her side and comfort her is Ben. He kisses her forehead and promises he will never leave her. It would be easy to think he is just saying it to make her feel better, but I know the truth. I know that he will never, ever leave her no matter what. She means the world to him.

I know this man is the person I will spend the rest of my life with. He's my other half, and my soulmate. He will never intentionally hurt me, because he supports everything I ever do and makes me believe that some people are faithful, even with all the relationship horror stories I hear. I tell clients all the time that true love exists, good people exist, and not everyone in life has the 'unfaithful gene'.

I want to marry Ben. I want to be his wife, and I want more than anything to share the rest of my life with him. I see old people who are still in love: they can hardly walk but they hold their partner's hand like they'll never let go. That's going to be us, I know it is. I've been through one wrong marriage, and I believe that makes me more qualified to judge that this time I've found the right person.

It's such a bitter irony now to be faced with the decision I have to make. Why can't I have it all? The perfect man and the perfect job. No drama, no dilemmas, just to be settled and happy. I used to believe I craved drama, but now I know I don't want it. At one point in life I think it was an addiction – the more drama the better. Just as I kick the addiction, and know deep down and truly come to terms with the fact I want no more drama, more is thrown in my way!

My job is part of my life, it's me through and through. This is my lifestyle choice, not my *occupation*. Outside it's spring and there are daffodils popping up. The early morning sky is a dusky pink colour. Suddenly the answer comes to me. Surely there's a compromise I can make? Maybe if I step back from the front-line investigation and focus on the marketing side of the business instead, Ben's bosses will start to accept that? I'd quite like to give up the late nights and unpredictable hours once we're married, so I can spend more time with my new little family. The girls can easily handle the investigations while I focus on publicising us.

If it comes down to it and I have to choose, Ben will win every single time. I have the love of the most amazing man in the world, and nothing will ever make me give that up. But I do feel a compromise can be made, and perhaps this is it.

It's a eureka moment! Fingers crossed they accept this, and maybe I can have it all – the whole package. Great family, great home life, great job, and I won't let down the people in need who turn to us at their worst moments.

Upstairs I can hear Paris rushing in to wake Ben and I'm about to join them when I hear the phone ring – the out-of-hours phone with the James Bond ring tone.

'Hello, The Lady Detective Agency … No, I agree … Yes, it's hard to see why your husband would have a red lipstick in his glove compartment … Yes, of course. I expect we can probably help …'

For more on The Lady Detective Agency and the services we offer, see our website www.ladydetectiveagency.com

---

ACKNOWLEDGEMENTS

Dedications of a book are supposed to be short … but I break the rules! This is my first book! Stay with it!

My beautiful husband – thank you for restoring all my faith in love, trust and human nature! You are the whole reason I can do what I do and be so happy along the way! Your support is the only thing that's got me where I am.

The parentals – I got Daddy's brain for business, and the mother's crazy streak! I wouldn't have it any other way! Thank you for all your love and support, I wouldn't have got through the hardest times without you being the amazing parents you are.

The ladies! – you'll always have my eternal gratitude for everything you do and have done!

Jen Jen – you entered my life as my agent, and implanted yourself as my friend! Thank you for being my sounding board every darn day, and for your sheer passion/belief in everything I do! I'll never forget those words: 'Write me a bit of something, and let's see what happens …'

Charlotte and Lesley from Aitken Alexander, Annie and the Arlington Enterprise ladies, Natalie and the Harper team – thank you for your belief in the crazy train. You turned my dream into reality … Or rather the reality into a dream!

My brother, Tony, Joanne, Lewis, 'Sister', Maria, Olivia, Judith, Pete and Jakey!

My Grandma and Granddad – who always knew I'd be a 'writer'!!!

The Angel and Peaches – one day you'll understand Mummy's crazy life. I hope when you get older this book will inspire you to follow your dreams, because just like my mummy and daddy, that's all I want you to do.